A B

CW3

Other Titles of Interest

BP44   IC 555 Projects
BP88   How to Use Op Amps
BP266 Electronic Modules and Systems for Beginners
BP273 Practical Electronic Sensors
BP299 Practical Electronic Filters
BP321 Circuit Source – Book 1
BP322 Circuit Source – Book 2
BP333 A Beginners Guide to CMOS Digital IC's

A BEGINNERS GUIDE TO TTL DIGITAL IC'S

by

R. A. PENFOLD

**BERNARD BABANI (publishing) LTD
THE GRAMPIANS
SHEPHERDS BUSH ROAD
LONDON W6 7NF
ENGLAND**

Please Note

Although every care has been taken with the production of this book to ensure that any projects, designs, modifications and/or programs, etc., contained herewith, operate in a correct and safe manner and also that any components specified are normally available in Great Britain, the Publishers do not accept responsibility in any way for the failure, including fault in design, of any project, design, modification or program to work correctly, or to cause damage to any other equipment that it may be connected to or used in conjunction with, or in respect of any other damage or injury that may be so caused, nor do the Publishers accept responsibility in any way for the failure to obtain specified components.

Notice is also given that if equipment that is still under warranty is modified in any way or used or connected with home-built equipment then that warranty may be void.

© 1993 BERNARD BABANI (publishing) LTD

First Published — November 1993

British Library Cataloguing in Publication Data
Penfold, R. A.
    Beginners Guide to TTL Digital IC's
    I. Title
    621.3815

    ISBN 0 85934 332 4

Printed and Bound in Great Britain by Cox & Wyman Ltd, Reading

Preface

TTL logic integrated circuits have been available to electronics hobbyists for well over twenty years now. In the early days they were not particularly popular, but for most hobbyists digital electronics was something new. The change from analogue to digital circuits took some time, but by the early 1970s many electronics enthusiasts were conversant with digital concepts, and were building digital projects. TTL integrated circuits had really "taken off", and they were used in vast numbers. Despite advances in electronics, TTL integrated circuits remain very popular. Although the original TTL devices are now largely obsolete, they have been replaced by various improved versions which are pin-for-pin compatible with the originals. Many new devices have been added over the years, and the full TTL range is now vast. To a large extent the world of digital electronics still revolves around the range of TTL devices.

This book first covers the basics of simple logic circuits in general, and then progresses to specific TTL logic integrated circuits. The devices covered include gates, oscillators, timers, flip/flops, dividers, and decoder circuits. Some practical circuits are used to illustrate the use of TTL devices in "real world" applications. The reader is not assumed to have any previous knowledge of logic circuits and techniques, but is presumed to have some general background knowledge of electronics.

R. A. Penfold

Contents

Page

Chapter 1
LOGIC CONCEPTS 1
In a State 1
Gates 2
Practical Gates 8
Inverting Gates 11
Buffers 13
Trigger Happy 15

Chapter 2
PRACTICAL TTL GATES 19
What Is TTL? 19
The Real Thing 19
LS TTL 23
CMOS 26
Micro Power 27
High Speed CMOS 30
Which TTL? 32
Static-Sensitive 33
Practical Gates 35

Chapter 3
OSCILLATORS AND TIMERS 43
Limitations 43
Basic Astable 44
Trigger Oscillator 48
Crystal Oscillators 49
TTL VCO 55
555 Oscillator 57
Signal Gate 58
Gated Astables 59
Two-Phase Outputs 62
Monostables 65
555 Monostable 71
Practical Circuits 72
Pulsed Tone Generators 73
F.M. Alarm Generator 77

Chapter 3 (Continued)   **Page**
    Analogue Frequency Meter 79
    Logic Probe 83

Chapter 4
    FLIP/FLOPS AND DIVIDERS 87
    Basic Flip/Flops 87
    "D" Type Flip/Flop 88
    Ripple Counters 93
    Divide by Ten 98
    Crystal Calibrator 103
    Heads or Tails 107
    Metronome 112
    Electronic Timer 115

Chapter 5
    DECODING 119
    Gates 120
    Comparators 121
    Input Selector 125
    3 to 8 Line 127
    Data Latches 131
    Octal Inputs 135
    PC Port 137
    TTL Power Supplies 140

Chapter 1

LOGIC CONCEPTS

There is a minor obstacle for anyone learning the basics of logic circuits, which is simply that the basic building blocks of logic circuits appear to be very clever, but of no real practical value. The functions of logic gates, decoders, etc., are easy enough to understand, but they can seem to be rather remote from "real world" applications. In reality, logic circuits are genuinely useful in numerous practical applications. A substantial percentage of the electronic gadgets currently on sale are totally digital in nature, or contain a substantial amount of digital circuitry. Applications which were once strictly the domain of analogue circuits are increasingly being taken over by digital circuits. In the world of hi-fi for instance, compact discs and other digital recording systems have to a large extent ousted analogue recording methods. The control circuits of many pieces of hi-fi equipment are also largely digital.

Logic circuits do not lend themselves well to all applications, and this is something that circuit designers need to bear in mind. Practically any electronic function can be performed using a logic based circuit, but in many instances this would be doing things the hard way. As with any design work, it is a matter of considering all the options, and choosing the most practical solution to the problem.

In a State
The fundamental difference between logic and analogue circuits is that the analogue variety are designed to handle signal levels that can be anywhere between certain maximum and minimum levels. Logic circuits operate on the basis of just two signal levels. These are logic 0 ("low") and logic 1 ("high"). The exact voltage ranges that count as valid logic 0 and logic 1 signals depend on the particular logic devices used, and in many cases are also dependent on the supply voltage used. Most digital circuits operate from a 5 volt supply, and a valid logic 0 level would typically be between

1

0 and 2 volts. A valid logic 1 level would be from about 3 volts to 5 volts.

With all the common families of logic integrated circuits there is a range of voltages between the maximum acceptable logic 0 level and the minimum acceptable logic 1 level. For reliable operation it is important that logic outputs do not provide output voltages within this invalid voltage range. The way in which a logic input will respond to an invalid input voltage is unpredictable. In many cases the input voltage will be accepted as a valid logic level, but there is no way of predicting which logic level will be attributed to an in-between voltage. In some cases the logic device fed with the invalid input potential will produce an equally invalid output voltage. This is unlikely though, and instability at the output (usually in the form of high frequency oscillation) is the more likely result.

Invalid voltages are not a major problem provided the circuit designer does not try to mix integrated circuits from different logic families. There is actually good compatibility between certain logic families, but it is a point that should be checked before using a mixture of logic types. Another potential cause of problems is where two logic circuits having different supply voltages must be connected together. This is generally only possible with the aid of a simple level shifter circuit.

A third point to be wary of is loading logic outputs to the point where they provide invalid output voltages. This can occur if, for instance, a l.e.d. indicator is driven from a logic output. Using an excessive l.e.d. current can load the output so heavily that it will not produce a valid logic 1 output level. If the l.e.d. is the only thing that is driven from the logic output this might not matter too much, although it is advisable always to keep the loading on any circuit within the normal design limits. If an output is also used to drive a logic input, then it should definitely not be loaded so heavily that an invalid output level is produced.

Gates

The most simple of the logic building blocks are the gates. Figure 1.1 shows the circuit symbols for a selection of logic

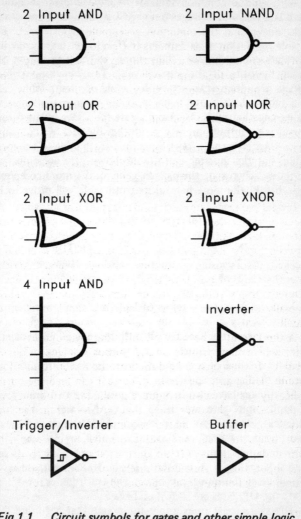

Fig. 1.1 Circuit symbols for gates and other simple logic devices (inputs on the left, outputs on the right)

gates, plus one or two other simple logic devices. Note that the more complex logic integrated circuits do not have special circuit symbols, and like any other complex integrated circuits, they are simply represented by rectangles on circuit diagrams.

The most simple gate is the NOT type, or inverter as it is more commonly known. This simply provides an output that is the opposite of the input level. The functions of logic devices are often explained with the aid of a truth table. This is a table which shows every possible combination of input states, together with the output state (or states in the case of a multiple output circuit) produced by each set of input levels. An inverter is too simple for a truth table to be worthwhile, but the inverter truth table shown here does illustrate the basic scheme of things. In general, the more complex a logic block, the more helpful its truth table will prove to be.

Inverter Truth Table

INPUT	OUTPUT
Low	High
High	Low

Inverters may seem to be of little real value, but they are actually used a great deal in practical circuits. Logic circuit designers are often faced with outputs that go high when a low signal level is required, and vice versa. Adding an inverter provides a signal of the required type. Inverters are also much used in oscillator circuits.

Most gates have two or more inputs. The two basic forms of multi-input gate are the 2 input AND and 2 input OR varieties. The output of a 2 input AND gate is high when both input 1 and input 2 are high, but is low for any other combination of input levels. The output of a 2 input OR gate is high when input 1 or input 2 (or both) are high, but is low if neither of the inputs are high. The truth tables for 2 input AND and OR gates are shown on page 5.

The same basic rules apply for a gate that has more than two inputs. For a 3 input AND gate for example, the output is high if input 1, input 2, and input 3 are high, but is low for

2 Input AND Gate Truth Table

INPUT 1	INPUT 2	OUTPUT
Low	Low	Low
Low	High	Low
High	Low	Low
High	High	High

2 Input OR Gate Truth Table

INPUT 1	INPUT 2	OUTPUT
Low	Low	Low
Low	High	High
High	Low	High
High	High	High

any other combination of input states. The output of a 4 input OR gate is high if input 1 or input 2 or input 3 or input 4 is high, but is low if none of the inputs is high. This truth table is for a 4 input AND gate.

4 Input AND Gate Truth Table

INPUT 1	INPUT 2	INPUT 3	INPUT 4	OUTPUT
Low	Low	Low	Low	Low
Low	Low	Low	High	Low
Low	Low	High	Low	Low
Low	Low	High	High	Low
Low	High	Low	Low	Low
Low	High	Low	High	Low
Low	High	High	Low	Low
Low	High	High	High	Low
High	Low	Low	Low	Low
High	Low	Low	High	Low
High	Low	High	Low	Low
High	Low	High	High	Low
High	High	Low	Low	Low
High	High	Low	High	Low
High	High	High	Low	Low
High	High	High	High	High

There is a variation on the AND gate called the NAND gate. This is effectively just an AND gate with an inverter added at the output. Consequently, for a given set of input states it will provide the opposite output state to an AND gate. It therefore provides a low output level if all the inputs are high, but a high output level for any other combination of input states.

Similarly, a NOR gate is a variation on the OR gate, and it is effectively an OR gate with an inverter added at the output. Therefore, the output goes low if one or more of the inputs is high, or is high if the inputs are all low. These are the truth tables for 2 input NAND and NOR gates, plus the truth table for a 4 input NAND gate.

2 Input NAND Gate Truth Table

INPUT 1	INPUT 2	OUTPUT
Low	Low	High
Low	High	High
High	Low	High
High	High	Low

2 Input NOR Gate Truth Table

INPUT 1	INPUT 2	OUTPUT
Low	Low	High
Low	High	Low
High	Low	Low
High	High	Low

4 Input NAND Gate Truth Table

INPUT 1	INPUT 2	INPUT 3	INPUT 4	OUTPUT
Low	Low	Low	Low	High
Low	Low	Low	High	High
Low	Low	High	Low	High
Low	Low	High	High	High

(Continued)

INPUT 1	INPUT 2	INPUT 3	INPUT 4	OUTPUT
Low	High	Low	Low	High
Low	High	Low	High	High
Low	High	High	Low	High
Low	High	High	High	High
High	Low	Low	Low	High
High	Low	Low	High	High
High	Low	High	Low	High
High	Low	High	High	High
High	High	Low	Low	High
High	High	Low	High	High
High	High	High	Low	High
High	High	High	High	Low

There is another variation on the OR gate, and this is the Exclusive OR (XOR) type. The output of an ordinary 2 input OR gate goes high if input 1 or input 2 goes high. However, it also goes high if both input 1 and input 2 go high, rather than just one or the other of them. With an exclusive OR gate the output only goes high if just one input goes high. Any other set of input states results in the output assuming the low state. An exclusive OR gate therefore provides what could reasonably be regarded as a true OR gate function. An exclusive NOR (XNOR) gate provides the same basic function as an exclusive OR gate, but has an inverted output. Exclusive OR and exclusive NOR gates do not seem to be used a great deal in practical applications, but they do have their uses. These are the truth tables for 2 input exclusive OR and exclusive NOR gates, plus the truth table for a 3 input exclusive OR gate.

2 Input XOR Gate Truth Table

INPUT 1	INPUT 2	OUTPUT
Low	Low	Low
Low	High	High
High	Low	High
High	High	Low

2 Input XNOR Gate Truth Table

INPUT 1	INPUT 2	OUTPUT
Low	Low	High
Low	High	Low
High	Low	Low
High	High	High

3 Input XOR Gate Truth Table

INPUT 1	INPUT 2	INPUT 3	OUTPUT
Low	Low	Low	Low
Low	Low	High	High
Low	High	Low	High
Low	High	High	Low
High	Low	Low	High
High	Low	High	Low
High	High	Low	Low
High	High	High	Low

Practical Gates

Gates are used a great deal in logic circuits, and there are probably few practical digital circuits which do not include a few gates. Even if there are no gate integrated circuits present in the circuit, there will almost certainly be dozens of them hidden away in the internal circuits of more complex logic devices. Although gates may not seem to be particularly useful, they are essential to simple decision making tasks in many practical applications.

As a very simple example, we will consider a security light application where a passive infra-red detector circuit will switch on the light when someone is detected within the protected zone. It is normal for devices of this type to switch on the light only during the hours of darkness. At other times the lamp is superfluous, and there would be little point in switching it on. A light detector circuit is therefore used to detect whether or not the ambient light level is low enough to make it worthwhile switching on the light.

Suppose that the light detector circuit produces a high output level when the light level is low enough to warrant switching on the lamp, and that the infra-red detector provides a high output level when someone is detected within the monitored area. Obviously the lamp driver circuit must only be activated when the outputs from the light detector and the infra-red detector are both high. Assuming that the lamp will be switched on by a high logic level at the input of the driver circuit, a 2 input AND gate will give the desired gating action. The output of a 2 input AND gate only goes high if both inputs are high. The lamp would therefore only be switched on if the light level was low enough and someone was detected in the monitored zone.

In a practical unit of this type a timer circuit would also be needed. The output from the infra-red sensor circuit will be a series of pulses while someone is within the monitored zone, not a constant high output level. The timer ensures that the lamp is held in the on state between pulses from the infra-red sensor, but the lamp will only remain switched on for a few seconds once the monitored area has been vacated. Some extra signal processing of this type is often needed in "real world" applications in order to obtain satisfactory results. As we shall see in a later chapter, there are special logic devices which can be used in a wide variety of timing applications. The final setup used in the automatic security light would be something along the lines of the arrangement shown in the block diagram of Figure 1.2.

Whatever set of input levels must be detected, and whatever output state is required when the input conditions are met, there is always a gate or combination of gates that will provide the desired result. In our example gate problem, if a low output level was needed when the inputs were both high, a NAND gate would be suitable. If the light detector gave a low output level when darkness was detected, things would be a bit more awkward. The state to be detected would be with one input high and one input low. An important point to keep in mind here is that although we have been talking in terms of input 1, input 2, etc., the inputs of a gate are treated identically. The numbering of gate inputs is therefore purely arbitrary, and input 1 is whichever input you

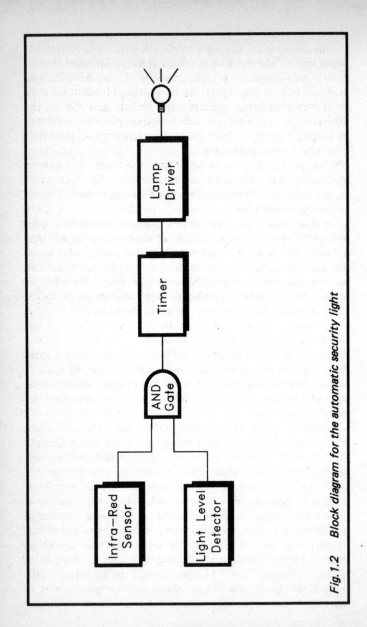

Fig.1.2   Block diagram for the automatic security light

decide to call input 1.

On the face of it, an exclusive OR gate could be used to solve this example problem. With input 1 high and input 2 low it would provide a high output level. With both inputs low and both inputs high it would provide a low output level. In reality a 2 input exclusive OR gate is unusable in this situation, as it will also provide a high output level if input 1 is low and input 2 is high (i.e. if it is daylight and there is no one within the monitored area).

The easiest solution to this type of problem is to use an AND gate, but to add an inverter ahead of the input which is low when in the active state. This gives the desired result, and only requires the addition of a simple inverter. An AND gate plus some inverters is a very potent combination, since it can be used to detect any desired set of input states. Any inputs which are active high are connected straight through to the gate, while any that are active low are fed to the gate via an inverter. Figure 1.3 shows a gate/inverter circuit of this type which will provide a low output level only when the top three inputs are low, and the bottom three are high.

Inverting Gates

Some gates can be used as inverters, and this property is often exploited in practical circuits. There may seem to be little point in using gates in this way, but in practical circuits there are often some spare gates. This is simply because there are usually two, three, or four of the more simple gates per integrated circuit. If you only require one or two 2 input NAND gates for example, you still have to use a quad 2 input NAND integrated circuit, which leaves two or three spare gates. Where applicable, it clearly makes sense to use these as inverters, rather than provide the inverters using an additional integrated circuit. On the other hand, I would not advocate the practice of using up superfluous gates just for the sake of it. There is nothing to be gained by finding ways of working spare gates, etc., into a circuit, and it is quite in order to simply leave surplus logic blocks unused.

The types of gate that can be used as inverters are the NAND and NOR varieties. There is no way of obtaining an inverter action from OR and AND gates. One way of using

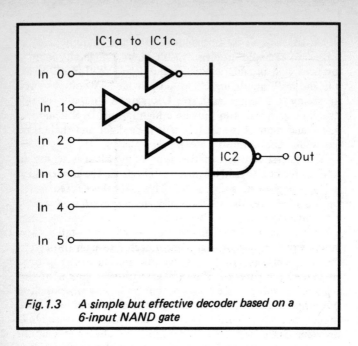

Fig. 1.3   A simple but effective decoder based on a 6-input NAND gate

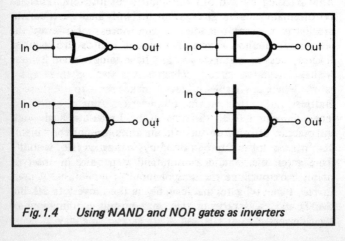

Fig. 1.4   Using NAND and NOR gates as inverters

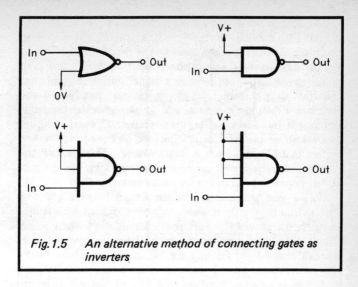

Fig. 1.5   An alternative method of connecting gates as inverters

NAND and NOR gates as inverters is to simply wire their inputs together (Figure 1.4). As reference to the truth tables provided earlier will show, the output will always take up the opposite state to the inputs. There is a slight drawback in this method in that an inverter of this type loads down the driving circuit by two or more inputs, not just one. This will not normally matter, since problems with inadequate fanout are quite rare with modern logic devices. However, the alternative method shown in Figure 1.5 gives the required inverter action, but only loads the driving circuit by one input.

Buffers
There is a limit to the number of inputs that a single logic output can drive properly. The maximum number of inputs that can be driven from an output is known as the "fanout". The fanout figure varies substantially depending on the type of logic output, and the type of input or inputs that it must drive. Fanout figures are generally in the range 5 to 50, but can be as low as one or two with certain combinations of logic devices.

The fanout of a logic circuit block can effectively be increased by feeding its output to one or more buffers. In an electronic and computing context the word "buffer" has a number of meanings, but in the present context it is a logic circuit element that can provide a higher output current than a normal device from that particular logic family. It can therefore drive more inputs, and gives higher than normal fanout. In fact some buffers do not have high current output stages, but are instead meant to be used on the basis of several buffers being driven from a single source. This gives several outputs, and the inputs are shared out amongst the outputs so that no output has its fanout figure exceeded.

Unless you get involved in the design of very complex digital circuits you are unlikely to have problems with fanout figures being exceeded. Buffers are mainly used where something other than a logic input must be driven, or where devices from different logic families are being used together. In the past buffers have often been used where a l.e.d. indicator or a l.e.d. display of some kind must be driven. These days buffer stages to drive l.e.d.s are often unnecessary, since high brightness l.e.d.s and l.e.d. displays are available at low prices. Also, many logic devices that are intended for use with l.e.d. displays have built-in buffers at the appropriate outputs. Buffers can still be useful though. There are two types of buffer incidentally, which are inverting and non-inverting types.

It is sometimes necessary to have two or more outputs driving a single input. Simply wiring two or more normal logic outputs directly together is not an acceptable practice. Apart from the fact that the results would be rather unpredictable, there would be a danger of the components passing an excessive output current and sustaining damage. Often the problem can be solved by using a gate to effectively combine several outputs to produce a single output signal. In some cases though, it is necessary to have several outputs, with only one of these switched through to an input at any one time.

In some simple applications a mechanical switch might be the most appropriate solution. In most cases though, some form of electronic switching is needed. This can be achieved using several three state (or "tristate") buffers. As already explained, a normal logic circuit can produce only two output

14

states (high and low). A tristate buffer has the ability to produce a third output state, which is a high impedance type. In other words, the output is effectively switched off, and it will go to whatever logic level is dictated by another (active) output. When in this "off" state a tristate output is in many ways more like an input, and to the circuit driving the buffer it "looks" much like an input in terms of the loading it provides.

A tristate buffer has two inputs. One of these is the normal input, and the output goes high or low depending on the logic level at this input. The second input can force the output into the high impedance state. Some tristate buffers require this input to be taken high in order to switch off the output; others require it to be taken low. The only way to determine which method applies to a particular device is to consult the relevant data sheet.

The normal method of using tristate buffers is shown in Figure 1.6. In this example there are four tristate buffers feeding into a single input. The control logic circuit determines which of the four buffers drives the input at a given time. It is obviously essential to have a well designed control logic circuit that will never activate two or more buffers simultaneously. Ideally the control signals should be provided by a device which is only capable of activating one buffer at a time.

Trigger Happy

Ideally the input signal to a logic circuit should always switch cleanly and very rapidly from one logic level to the other. In practice this should always occur when one logic device is used to drive another. Problems can arise when a logic input is driven from a source such as a temperature or light level detector. The output of such a circuit will often switch from one logic level to the other at a relatively low rate. This results in the output being in the region between acceptable logic 0 and logic 1 levels for too long.

This will not invariably cause problems, and some logic devices are more tolerant of this sort of thing than others. However, it can result in instability as the output passes through the invalid voltage range, and it is advisable to guard

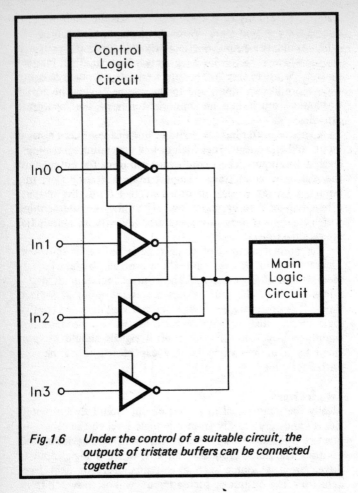

Fig. 1.6 *Under the control of a suitable circuit, the outputs of tristate buffers can be connected together*

against this problem by using a trigger circuit.

A trigger circuit has a high degree of hysteresis, which is basically just a reluctance for the output to revert to its old state once it has switched to a new state. With a non-inverting trigger circuit it usually requires about two-thirds of the supply voltage at the input in order to take the output to the high logic state. Taking the input back below two-thirds of the supply voltage will not result in the output reverting to the low state. Instead, the input will typically need to be taken below about one-third of the supply voltage in order to force the output back to the low state. With one switching threshold voltage there is a tendency for the circuit to become unstable when the input voltage is close to this threshold level. Having two threshold voltages with a wide gap between them avoids this problem.

Some gates and other logic devices have built-in trigger circuits at their inputs. In most cases though, separate trigger circuits have to be added ahead of logic inputs if there might be problems with a slowly changing input voltage. Devices containing several trigger circuits (which are usually of the inverting variety) are readily available. If in doubt about the switching speed of an input signal it is advisable to play safe and include a trigger circuit.

Chapter 2

PRACTICAL TTL GATES

In Chapter 1 the general subject of logic gates and other simple logic building blocks was discussed. In this chapter we will cover what is essentially the same subject, but as it applies to practical TTL logic integrated circuits.

What Is TTL?
Before considering some practical TTL devices it would be as well to clarify what exactly we mean by TTL logic integrated circuits. TTL is an acronym, and it stands for "transistor transistor logic". It is one of the original logic families, with its origins back in the 1960s. Other popular logic families in those days were the RTL (resistor transistor logic) and DTL (diode transistor logic) varieties. These names indicate the types of component that are central to the operation of each logic family. The TTL devices were always much more popular than those from the other two logic families, and by the early 1970s both the RTL and DTL devices were obsolete.

Although the original TTL components have survived into the 1990s, and with a few exceptions they are still readily available, they are now obsolete as well. The standard TTL logic devices are mainly sold as spares for old equipment, or for use in newly constructed equipment that is being built to an old design. Various "improved" TTL families have appeared over the years, and these have to a large extent ousted the standard devices which are little used in new designs. To be more accurate, some of the families of "improved" TTL integrated circuits have ousted the standard type. Several of the families of "improved" TTL devices have serious shortcomings. This has led to some of these logic families barely surviving, while others have sunk without trace.

The Real Thing
Before looking at the more important of the "improved" TTL families, it would be as well to consider the ordinary TTL integrated circuits. These have plenty of good points, but

have some major drawbacks as well. The standard range of TTL integrated circuits are based on ordinary n.p.n. bipolar transistors, and an important consequence of this is that they have quite high levels of current consumption. Devices which contain a few simple gates consume around 20 milliamps, while some of the more complex devices draw supply currents of more than 100 milliamps. This makes standard TTL integrated circuits far from ideal in applications where portability and battery operation is required.

The situation is not helped by the fact that TTL based circuits should ideally be used on a 5 volt supply having a minimum accuracy of plus and minus 5% (i.e. a supply in the range of 4.75 volts to 5.25 volts). This is far from convenient if battery operation is required. In practice it is possible to use a 4.5 volt or 6 volt battery as the power source, but results are likely to be less than optimum if anything other than a well regulated 5 volt supply is used.

Another supply related problem is that TTL integrated circuits do not have good immunity to noise on the supply rails. Noise spikes on the supply can easily result in spurious operations of the TTL devices in a circuit. A well regulated 5 volt supply will help to minimise this problem, but it is also necessary to use plenty of supply decoupling capacitors. With large circuits it is normal to use one 100n ceramic decoupling capacitor for every three or four TTL integrated circuits. These capacitors should be distributed as evenly across the circuit board as possible. Some circuit designers seem to take a no compromise approach, and use one decoupling capacitor per TTL device, with each capacitor mounted close to its particular integrated circuit. This probably represents severe overkill, but it is one way of ensuring that supply noise problems are totally avoided.

Although TTL integrated circuits were popular from the outset, they have always had something less than universal acceptance. Their awkward power supply requirements probably represent the main reason that some circuit designers were reluctant to use them. Even where battery operation was not required, a mains power supply providing a well stabilised 5 volts at currents of a few amps was often needed. While such a supply was not technically difficult to produce, it did tend to be quite expensive.

TTL devices had a big advantage over most other early logic integrated circuits in that they could provide what, at that time anyway, was very high speed operation. In fact the standard TTL devices are respectably fast even by current standards. The maximum usable operating frequency varies significantly from one device to another, and in general the simpler components can operate at higher speeds than the complex devices. Maximum operating frequencies are typically around 30MHz to 40MHz, which is obviously more than adequate for most applications.

The internal circuit diagrams of many integrated circuits are not made available by the manufacturers, but the range of TTL logic devices is an exception. All the circuits are freely available, but many of them look rather odd. The circuits are unconventional in that free use is made of transistors having multiple emitter terminals. In particular, transistors having two or more emitters often seem to be used at the inputs of gates. The circuit of Figure 2.1 for example, is for one of the four 2 input NAND gates in a 7400. As will be apparent from this circuit, each input is taken to a different emitter terminal of the same transistor.

Although the circuits may look rather odd, they are mostly quite straightforward in operation. In this case, taking either emitter (or both) low results in R1 biasing TR1 into conduction. This diverts the base current away from TR2, which then switches off, as does TR4 which previously pulled the output terminal low. The output is now pulled high by TR3, which is an emitter follower buffer stage driven from the output of TR2. The required NAND gate action is therefore obtained, with the output going low if both inputs are high. Any other set of input levels results in the output going high. In normal use the inputs of all devices should be taken to a definite logic level, and not simply left floating. However, if a TTL input should be left floating, it normally drifts to what is effectively the high state.

The type of output stage used in the NAND gate circuit of Figure 2.1 is typical of TTL integrated circuits, and is known as a "totem pole" output stage. It does not consume very much output current with the output high, or with it low.

21

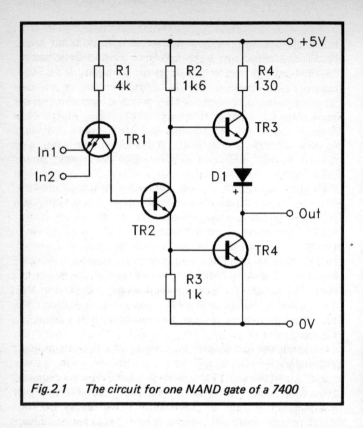

Fig.2.1   The circuit for one NAND gate of a 7400

Either way, one or other of the output transistors will be switched off, and little current will flow through these two components. The relatively high current of standard TTL devices is due to the current that flows through the input and driver stages.

It is possible to alter the resistor values to produce lower supply currents, and this is basically what was done to produce the low power TTL series of devices. The original TTL integrated circuits have a "74" prefix, followed by a two or three digit serial number (e.g. 74138). The low power versions have the same basic type numbers, but with a "74L" prefix (e.g. "74L138).

Reducing the current consumption results in components that are much better suited to battery operation, but it also produces a reduction in the maximum operating frequency. This reduction in maximum operating frequency is far larger than one might expect. The 74L series have maximum operating frequencies of about 3MHz, which is something under one-tenth of the figure for standard TTL components. The current consumption was reduced by a similar amount incidentally. The low power TTL devices never achieved any degree of popularity, and this is probably due to the fact that their characteristics did not compare very favourably with the CMOS logic devices which came along in the early 1970s. They are now obsolete, and are probably unavailable even from suppliers of surplus components.

LS TTL

Of the "improved" TTL families that have stood the test of time, the most important is the LS (low power Schottky) type. These are the new standard range, and are the TTL devices which are most popular for use in new designs. The LS series of components use the same basic type numbers as the standard TTL components, but with a "74LS" prefix (e.g. 74LS138 is the low power Schottky equivalent of the original 74138 device).

74LS versions of TTL integrated circuits are a substantial improvement on the standard devices, as they achieve higher operating speeds but at significantly lower supply currents. The improved speed and reduced current consumption is made possible by the incorporation of Schottky diodes into the circuits. The circuit symbol for a Schottky diode is shown in Figure 2.2(a). These diodes are mainly used in conjunction with switching transistors in the manner shown in Figure 2.2(b). This combination is often given the circuit symbol of Figure 2.2(c).

The important difference between a Schottky diode and an ordinary silicon type is that it requires a forward voltage of only about 0.2 volts before it will start to conduct. This compares with a figure of about 0.5 to 0.6 volts for an ordinary silicon diode. They are also capable of high speed operation, which is crucial in the present application.

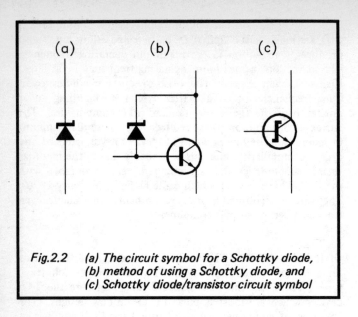

*Fig.2.2   (a) The circuit symbol for a Schottky diode,
            (b) method of using a Schottky diode, and
            (c) Schottky diode/transistor circuit symbol*

The speed of ordinary TTL integrated circuits is reduced by the fact that the switching transistors are biased into saturation. This gives problems with charge storage effects, and a slight reluctance for the transistors to switch off again. Higher operating speeds can be obtained if the base currents are regulated so that something only just beyond the minimum acceptable drive currents are used. This is achieved using a Schottky diode connected in the manner shown in Figure 2.2(b).

If the transistor is switched on to the point where its collector falls to about 0.4 volts, the Schottky diode becomes forward biased and starts to divert the base current through the collector circuit of the transistor. A diode having a fast switching speed is essential, as it must divert the excess base current before the transistor is able to saturate. It is also essential that the diode has a low forward conduction voltage. With an ordinary 0.6 volt switch-on potential the diode would not be biased into conduction until the transistor had been biased into saturation.

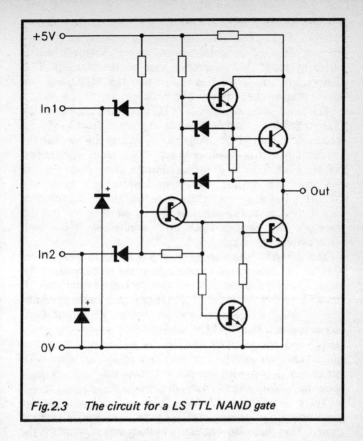

Fig.2.3   The circuit for a LS TTL NAND gate

The "74LS" circuits are not just the standard TTL types with a few Schottky diodes added. The circuits have been completely re-designed in order to fully exploit the advantages of Schottky diodes. Figure 2.3 shows the circuit diagram for one of the 2 input NAND gates in a 74LS00. This is clearly very different to the standard TTL NAND gate circuit of Figure 2.1. The use of diodes at the inputs harks back to the days of DTL logic integrated circuits.

Switching speeds of 74LS integrated circuits are only slightly better than those of the original TTL devices, being typically about 10 to 20% faster. This level of performance is achieved at only about a fifth of the standard TTL supply current though. The 74LS range therefore provides a substantial step forward in performance, and at a cost which is currently about 30% less than that of the standard TTL components. It is for this reason that the 74LS range has largely usurped the ordinary TTL devices.

There are other families of TTL integrated circuits which exploit Schottky diodes in order to obtain improved performance. The "74S" range have slightly higher current consumptions than their ordinary "74" series equivalents, but are some three to four times faster. Many devices in the 74S series can operate with input frequencies of well over 100MHz. For some time these were the fastest TTL components that were readily available, but as we shall see shortly, there are now devices which offer similar speeds but with lower current consumptions.

The "74ALS" (advanced low power Schottky) devices were at one time tipped to take over as the new standard TTL range. However, in reality they never achieved dominance of the TTL market, with the "LS" range providing the combination of price and performance that better suited most users' requirements. The "74ALS" devices are now something of a rarity, and are virtually obsolete. They achieve operating speeds that are nearly double those of the standard TTL components, but with current consumptions that are only about half those of the "74LS" devices.

There is also a "74AS" (advanced Schottky) range incidentally, but these never achieved a substantial market share. They have current consumptions which are much the same as the standard Schottky devices, but the maximum operating frequencies are in the region of 200MHz. This probably makes them the fastest TTL devices that have been produced commercially.

CMOS

CMOS is an acronym, and it stands for "complementary metal oxide silicon" (although some prefer "complementary metal oxide semiconductor"). Integrated circuits which are formed using this technology are based on enhancement mode MOSFETs ("metal oxide silicon field effect transistors"), and not ordinary bipolar transistors. As the "complementary" part of the name indicates, both N channel and P channel MOSFETs are used in these devices.

Looking at things from the users' standpoint, the main difference between an enhancement MOSFET and a bipolar transistor is that the latter is current operated whereas MOSFETs are voltage operated. A bipolar transistor remains switched off until the input voltage to the base terminal reaches about 0.6 volts. Up to this point very little current flows. Raising the input voltage above 0.6 volts results in a sudden increase in the base current, and the device begins to switch on. With an input potential of only about 0.7 volts the input current becomes quite large, and the device is switched on to saturation point. Taking the input voltage much higher is likely to cause an excessive base current, and the destruction of the transistor.

The forward transfer characteristic of an enhancement mode MOSFET is very different. These devices are switched off until the input voltage to the gate terminal reaches about 0.8 volts or so. Increasing the gate voltage above this level results in the device gradually switching on, with saturation point being reached at a gate potential of a few volts. The input resistance of a field effect transistor is extremely high, and in the case of a MOSFET it is often more than a million megohms (1 000 000 000 000 ohms). This means that the current flow into the gate of a MOSFET is negligible, and is actually far too low to measure using ordinary test equipment.

CMOS logic integrated circuits therefore have extremely high input resistances, and on the face of it they should have what is effectively infinite fanout capability. If high speed operation is not required, they do indeed have what for most practical purposes can be regarded as infinite fanout. If high speed operation is needed, the input capacitance must be taken into account. This gives increased loading at high frequencies which reduces the fanout figure to about 50. However, this is still so high that it is unlikely to be a limiting factor when designing practical CMOS logic circuits.

Micro Power
The very high input resistance of CMOS logic devices is a very

27

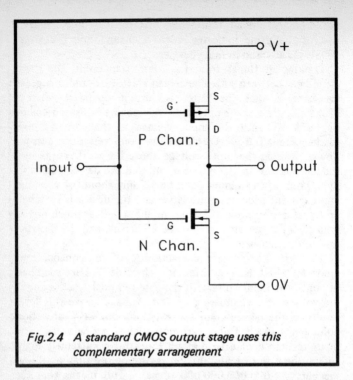

Fig.2.4 A standard CMOS output stage uses this complementary arrangement

useful characteristic, but their main advantage over most other types of logic integrated circuit is their low current consumption at low operating speeds. The output stages of CMOS integrated circuits consist of complementary (PMOS/NMOS) transistors which act as electronic switches. They are connected in the manner shown in Figure 2.4. When one of the transistors is switched on it has a resistance that is typically around 400 ohms. When one of the transistors is switched off it has a resistance that is extremely high (normally at least a thousand megohms). When an output is high it has a circuit equivalent to that of Figure 2.5(a), and while it is low it has a circuit equivalent to that of Figure 2.5(b).

The important point to note here is that in both cases the total resistance across the supply lines is extremely high, and will result in an insignificant current flow. On the face of it,

28

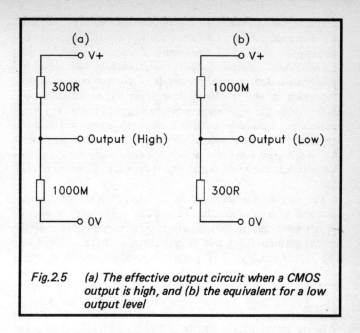

Fig.2.5 *(a) The effective output circuit when a CMOS output is high, and (b) the equivalent for a low output level*

CMOS logic integrated circuits have a negligible current consumption. Unfortunately, in reality matters are not quite as rosy as this. The first point to note is that any current which flows into a load connected at an output (a l.e.d. indicator for example) will be added to the normal current consumption of the device driving the load. The second point is that a pulse of current is consumed each time an output changes state. In effect, one switch is turned on to a significant degree before the other one switches off properly.

If a CMOS device is not driving a current through a load of some kind, and it is either static or operating at a very low frequency, it will draw an insignificant supply current. If it changes state at a high frequency there will be a large number of current pulses drawn from the supply in a given period of time, and a relatively high supply current. In general, the higher the operating frequency of a CMOS logic device, the higher the supply current it will consume. At low operating frequencies CMOS devices provide a massive power saving in comparison to standard TTL logic devices. At high frequencies it is possible for a CMOS device to have a higher current consumption than a TTL equivalent.

CMOS logic integrated circuits are therefore well suited to applications that require low levels of current consumption, and which involve relatively low operating frequencies. In reality they give significant power savings in practically any application, since few circuits have every stage operating at high speed. In "real world" circuits it is normally the case that some stages operate at high speed, while most of the others operate at low frequencies or are static for much of the time.

The original CMOS logic family (the "4000" series) was launched as a rival to the TTL range. The two ranges of devices were, and remain, almost totally incompatible. CMOS devices have relatively low output currents that can not drive TTL inputs reliably. TTL devices have ample output currents to drive CMOS inputs properly, but do not provide suitable high and low logic levels. Where similar devices exist in the two ranges, they almost invariably have different pinout configurations.

In the 1970s a range of CMOS TTL integrated circuits were introduced, and these had "74C" type numbers. However, these were really just standard CMOS circuits, but using the TTL pinout configurations. This made it easy for designers who were familiar with the TTL devices to produce circuits based on CMOS devices. Apart from this, the "74C" range provided no improvement in the compatibility of the two families of logic devices, and the "74C" series is now obsolete.

High Speed CMOS

The ordinary 4000 series of CMOS integrated circuits have a major limitation in that they will not operate at frequencies of more than a few megahertz. This gave CMOS and TTL integrated circuits their own market niches, with CMOS being used where low power consumption was more important than speed, and TTL being used where high speed was of paramount importance. These days there is an option which gives the best of both worlds. This is to use devices from one of the high speed CMOS logic families.

There are two common types, which are the "74HC" and "74HCT" series. These are both based on the same technology, and this technology is a refinement of the original CMOS type, rather than something completely new. It provides operation at far higher frequencies than the "4000" series can manage, and it also produces a much higher output current capability. The difference between the "74HC" and "74HCT" series is that the former operates at normal CMOS switching levels, whereas the latter operates at TTL logic levels.

The "4000" CMOS devices can operate over a supply voltage range of 3 to 15 volts, and the maximum logic 0 voltage is 30% of the supply voltage. The minimum logic 1 potential is 70% of the supply voltage. The "74HC" devices can only operate over a supply voltage range of 2 to 6 volts, and they are primarily intended for use in circuits that include components from the standard "4000" range. Of course, circuits can also be based solely on "74HC" series devices.

For TTL logic circuits the supply potential should normally be 5 volts, and the maximum acceptable logic 0 level is 0.8 volts. The minimum legitimate logic 1 level is 2 volts. The "74HCT" range are primarily intended for use in circuits that include devices from other TTL families. CMOS integrated circuits, unlike TTL devices, have good immunity to noise on the supply rails. The "74HC" range retain this excellent noist immunity, but the "74HCT" range does not. Therefore, if a circuit is to be based solely on high speed CMOS integrated circuits, the "74HC" series would seem to be a better choice than the "74HCT" range.

For both ranges of high speed CMOS devices the current consumption varies from a negligible level when static or operating at low frequencies, to a level that is comparable to equivalent "74LS" devices when operating at very high frequencies. The maximum operating frequency for high speed CMOS devices is much the same as for equivalent "74LS" components. There are advanced high speed CMOS devices which can operate at frequencies of over 100MHz (the "74AC" series), but as yet these are quite expensive, and difficult to obtain.

31

Which TTL?

With several types of TTL integrated circuit readily available, selecting the best type for a given application can be difficult. If you are following a published design, then it would clearly be advisable to use the exact types specified in the components list. If you are designing your own circuits, then "74LS" components would seem to be the obvious choice. It is probably only worth using a different type if the "74LS" devices are deficient in some way. If their current consumption is too high, then devices in the "74HCT" or "74HC" series would be a better choice, particularly if much of the circuit is operating at low frequencies, or in an intermittent fashion. Being realistic about matters, if low current consumption is important, and high operating speed is of no consequence, then "4000" series CMOS integrated circuits may well be a better choice than any TTL range. Where very high operating speeds are needed, "74ALS" or "74AC" devices should be suitable, if you can obtain them.

It has to be pointed out that the "74HC" and "74HCT" devices are starting to become cheaper than the "74LS" equivalents. We would seem to be reaching the point where using high speed CMOS components has become cheaper than using "74LS" types. If high speed CMOS components can be obtained more cheaply than the "74LS" types, then a circuit based solely on "74HC" devices is certainly the best choice. Possibly the "74LS" series will become largely obsolete over the next few years.

In general there is no difficulty in using a mixture of TTL types. The obvious exception is the "74HC" series, with its CMOS "4000" series logic levels. If high speed CMOS devices are used with other types of TTL integrated circuit, it is the "74HCT" range which must be utilized. The main reason for using a mixture of TTL types as an economy measure in a circuit where only certain stages need to operate at high frequencies. Devices from a high speed TTL range (e.g. "74ALS" types) would be used in the critical stages, with ordinary "74LS" or "74HCT" components being used elsewhere. Another reason for using a mixture of TTL types is that it is not always possible to find the devices you require in the appropriate TTL family. For example, the popular

74121 monostable only seems to be available as a standard TTL device, and is not available as a 74LS121, 74HCT121, etc.

The main point to watch when mixing TTL types is the fanout of the various devices in the circuit. With certain TTL combinations the fanout is very low indeed. In particular, 74HCT outputs can only drive two standard TTL inputs. This table shows the fanout for three common TTL families when used in any combination.

TTL Type (Driving)	Maximum No. of Inputs Driven		
	74	74LS	74HCT
74	10	40	100+
74 buffers	30	60	100+
74LS	5	20	100+
74LS buffers	15	60	100+
74HCT	2	10	100+
74HCT buffers	4	15	100+

Static-Sensitive

There is a slight drawback to the ultra-high input resistance of CMOS integrated circuits in that it makes them vulnerable to damage from high static voltages. Such voltages exist in normal environments, and the widespread use of plastics makes them more common than they might otherwise be. On the other hand, the risk of CMOS devices being damaged in this way is probably not particularly great. It is a risk which has perhaps been slightly exaggerated in the past. Some manufacturers have supplied integrated circuits in packets covered with dire warning notices. Some of these give the impression that the contents will be instantly "zapped" if the packet is opened outside a special anti-static chamber.

In reality, I (and many others) have used static-sensitive electronic components for many years without taking any elaborate anti-static precautions, and have never actually managed to "zap" one of these devices.

Some of the original "A" suffix CMOS logic chips were rather vulnerable to static damage, and some users did have failures which were probably attributable to static charges.

The built-in static protection circuits of the later "A" series devices were much improved. The modern "B" series components are even better, and if they are handled like ordinary non-static sensitive devices there is probably little risk of damage occurring. However, once any static-sensitive component is removed from its protective packing it makes sense to keep it away from any obvious source of static electricity. This mainly means keeping these components well away from computer monitors, large pieces of plastic, etc. When dealing with static-sensitive components it is obviously not a good idea to wear clothes made from 100% man-made fibres, especially if past experience suggests that they are good static generators. These days few clothes seem to be made from 100% man-made fibres, and those made from a mixture of natural and man-made fibres should be perfectly "safe".

These are the minimal precautions which should be taken when dealing with static-sensitive integrated circuits. First and foremost, leave the integrated circuits in their anti-static packing until it is time to fit them into place. This packing will usually be either a transparent plastic tube, or some form of conductive foam material. The purpose of the tubing is to insulate the pins from high static voltages. The conductive foam effectively places a short circuit across all the pins so that they will all be at the same voltage. Remember that it is a high voltage difference across two pins that is needed in order to "zap" a static-sensitive component, and not just a high voltage per se.

Do not fit the integrated circuits into place until the unit is finished in all other respects. It is a good idea to use holders for all d.i.l. integrated circuits, but they should be regarded as mandatory for static-sensitive types. If for some reason it should be necessary to solder a static-sensitive device directly to a circuit board, a soldering iron having an earthed bit should be used. Once a device has been removed from its protective packing it should be handled as little as possible. It is sometimes suggested that static-sensitive integrated circuits should be fitted into their holders without the pins being touched. This is rather unrealistic, because most d.i.l. integrated circuits require a fair amount of "friendly persuasion" before they will fit into their holders properly. In most cases the pins have to be pressed inwards slightly. However, it makes sense not to touch the pins any more than is really necessary.

If you wish to take more comprehensive precautions there are various anti-static aids available. These include wrist bands which you can use to earth yourself, and conductive work surfaces (which are also earthed in normal use). Being realistic about it, the cost of most CMOS logic integrated circuits is so low that, for the home constructor at any rate, the cost of anti-static equipment is likely to be many times greater than any cost savings it might produce. These anti-static gadgets are perhaps more attractive for commercial users, and (possibly) experimenters who will need to handle CMOS devices a good deal. However, having experimented with hundreds of CMOS integrated circuits I can not honestly say that I have ever found such gadgets necessary.

Practical Gates

Figures 2.6 to 2.9 give pinout details for some common TTL gates, buffers, and inverters. The list provided here shows most of the readily available CMOS gates and other simple devices. Some of these devices have "open collector" outputs. This is where the output terminal connects to the collector of an n.p.n. common emitter switching transistor, and there are no internal load components for this output transistor. A discrete load resistor must therefore be used. The normal application of open collector outputs is to provide a step-up from 5 volt logic levels to some other logic level. In the circuit of Figure 2.10 a step-up from 5 volt to 12 volt switching levels is achieved. Normal open collector outputs can handle supply potentials of up to 15 volts, but some can accommodate supplies of up to 30 volts.

AND Gates

7408	quad 2 input
7409	quad 2 input (open collector)
7411	triple 3 input
7421	dual 4 input

NAND Gates

| 7400 | quad 2 input |

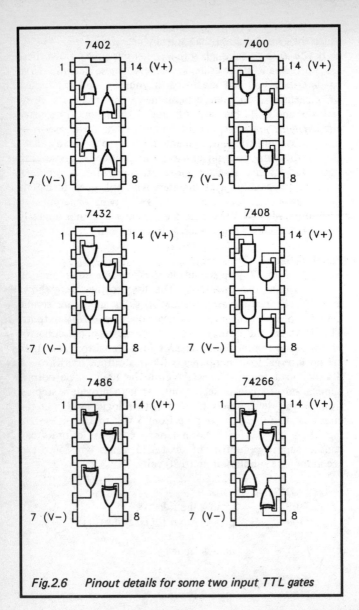

Fig.2.6   Pinout details for some two input TTL gates

7410	triple 3 input
7420	dual 4 input
7430	single 8 input

OR Gates

| 7432 | quad 2 input |

NOR Gates

7402	quad 2 input
7427	triple 3 input
7425	dual 4 input
7433	quad 2 input (open collector)

Others

7404	hex inverter
7407	hex buffer (open collector)
7417	hex buffer (open collector, 30V)
7486	quad 2 input XOR
74266	quad 2 input XNOR (open collector)
7414	hex inverting trigger
74125	quad tristate buffer (active low)
74126	quad tristate buffer (active high)
74244	octal tristate buffer
74245	octal transceiver

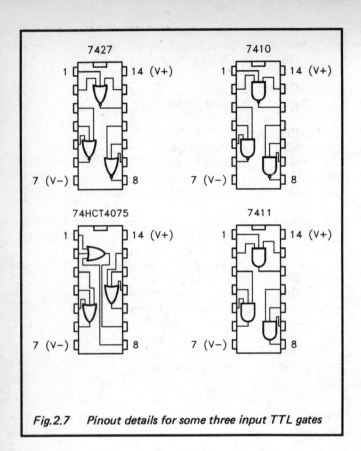

Fig.2.7   Pinout details for some three input TTL gates

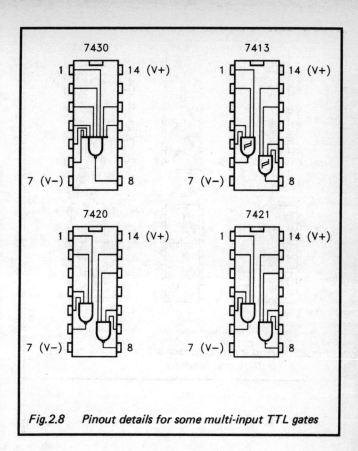

Fig. 2.8   Pinout details for some multi-input TTL gates

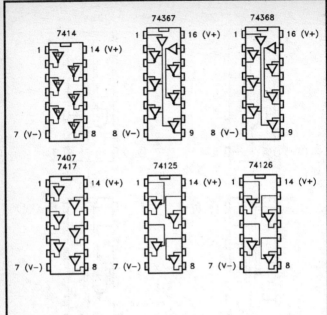

Fig. 2.9   Pinout details for some TTL buffers, tristate buffers, and inverters

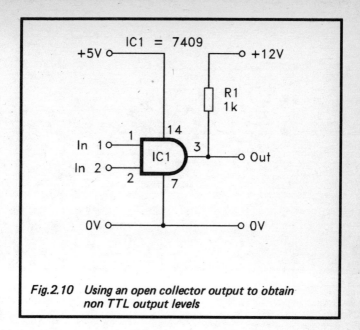

Fig.2.10 Using an open collector output to obtain non TTL output levels

41

Chapter 3

OSCILLATORS AND TIMERS

Oscillators and timing circuits play major roles in many electronic circuits, both analogue and digital types. Here we will obviously only be dealing with oscillators as they apply to TTL digital circuits, which means oscillators that provide pulsed output signals that are compatible with standard TTL and LS TTL inputs. Similarly, the timing circuits will provide output pulses that are compatible with TTL logic inputs.

Limitations

Simple oscillators are easily produced from TTL inverters or gates connected to act as inverters. It is only fair to point out that there are limitations to simple oscillators of this kind. They generally work quite well at audio frequencies, and above the audio range at frequencies of up to a few hundred kilohertz. Many simple TTL oscillators will actually work at much higher frequencies, possibly as high as a few megahertz. However, they are not necessarily usable at such high frequencies due to frequency drift, and the fact that the output frequency can not be set accurately. Where stable operation is needed at a high frequency, together with good frequency accuracy, a crystal oscillator should always be used. Some crystal oscillator circuits are featured in a later section of this chapter.

Another problem with simple TTL oscillators is that they can not operate with high value timing resistances. They differ in this respect from equivalent CMOS oscillators, and from most other C — R oscillators. The practical consequence of this is that they can not provide very low output frequencies. This can be overcome by using a divider circuit to derive a very low frequency output signal from a much higher frequency oscillator. However, as we shall see later in this chapter, it is often easier to resort to an oscillator circuit which is not based on TTL devices, but which has a TTL compatible output signal.

Basic Astable

Figure 3.1 shows the basic TTL astable multivibrator circuit. This is based on two inverters made from LS NAND gates (I would not recommend using standard TTL devices in this type of circuit as they might consume excessive supply currents). Looking at things in very simple terms, R1 biases IC1a and IC1b to act as a high gain amplifier which, overall, has the input and output in-phase. This fact, plus the high voltage gain of the amplifier, results in strong oscillation due to the positive feedback via C1. The operating frequency of the circuit is governed by the values of R1 and C1, and is very roughly equal to 1kHz with the specified values. Changes in

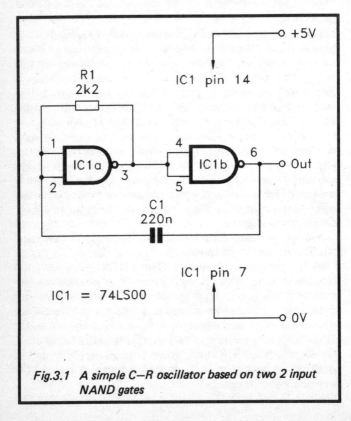

Fig.3.1   A simple C–R oscillator based on two 2 input
          NAND gates

44

the values of C1 and R1 have an inversely proportional affect on the output frequency (e.g. reducing C1 to 22n increases the output frequency to about 10kHz).

The value of R1 should not be changed much from the specified value of 2k2. In particular, values much higher than 2k2 are likely to result in the circuit failing to oscillate. It is best to use values in the range 820R to 2k2. The circuit will work well using a 74HC00, and due to the ultra-high input resistances of CMOS devices, high timing resistances can then be used. In fact a timing resistance of anything from 1k to 10M is acceptable. This makes it easy to obtain very low output frequencies.

C1 can have any value of more than about 100p, and ideally it should not be an electrolytic or other polarised type. However, without resorting to a polarised capacitor it is not possible to obtain output frequencies of less than about 100Hz using a 74LS00. Results seem to be satisfactory using an electrolytic capacitor connected with the polarity shown in Figure 3.2. I would not recommend using an electrolytic with a circuit based on a 74HC00, although this should not be necessary as the latter can produce low output frequencies without resorting to an electrolytic capacitor. It is advisable not to use very high values for C1, but frequencies down to a few hertz can be achieved using values up to about 47μ. The specified value of 22μ gives an output frequency of approximately 10 hertz. At the other end of the range the circuit will operate properly at frequencies of up to at least 500kHz. Oscillation at higher frequencies is possible, but as pointed out previously, at higher frequencies both frequency accuracy and stability tend to be problematic.

A few limitations need to be borne in mind when using this simple oscillator configuration. The main one is that the output frequency is not very predictable. Changing from one 74LS00 to another could result in the output frequency shifting upwards or downwards quite significantly. Also, the output frequency does change very slightly with variations in the supply voltage. This frequency change is probably not of great practical significance since the circuit will presumably be powered from a well stabilised supply. However, if a highly predictable and stable oscillator is required, it is probably best

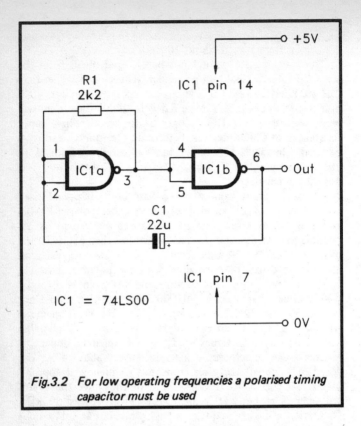

Fig.3.2 *For low operating frequencies a polarised timing capacitor must be used*

to resort to a higher quality oscillator circuit.

Another point to keep in mind is that the output waveform can not be guaranteed to have an accurate 1 to 1 mark-space ratio. The mark-space ratio will usually be quite close to 1 to 1, but in most cases there will be a small but significant imbalance in the output waveform. This is unimportant in many applications, but can occasionally be a crucial point.

Despite these limitations a simple TTL astable circuit is perfectly adequate for many simple applications. Some applications require anti-phase output signals, and this is easily achieved using another gate of the 74LS00 as a buffer/ inverter, as shown in Figure 3.3. Remember though,

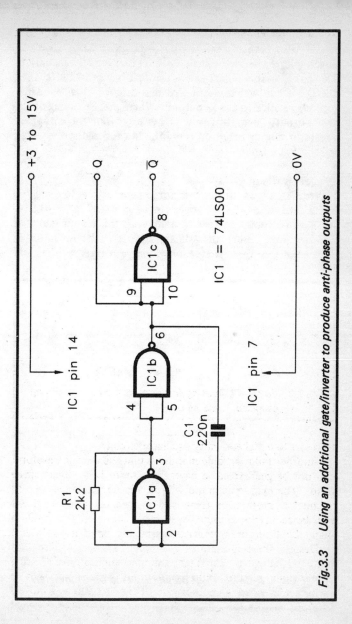

Fig.3.3   Using an additional gate/inverter to produce anti-phase outputs

47

that a simple circuit of this type is not adequate if the output signals must have accurate 1 to 1 mark-space ratios. It is also unsuitable if the two signals must switch exactly in unison. The not Q output signal passes through one more buffer than the Q output, which means that it is delayed by a few nanoseconds relative to the Q output. Where precise timing of the two outputs is important it is better to opt for anti-phase generator circuit based on the 74LS74 (as discussed in detail later in this chapter).

Trigger Oscillator

Figure 3.4 shows the circuit for a simple C — R oscillator based on one of the six trigger/inverter stages in a 74LS14. An essential point to keep in mind with this circuit is that it will not work using an ordinary inverter. Its operation is dependent on the inverter providing a trigger action, and

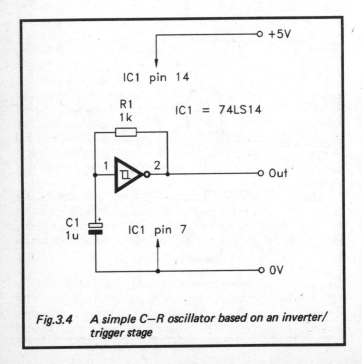

Fig.3.4   A simple C—R oscillator based on an inverter/
trigger stage

having a reasonable amount of hysteresis.

C1 has no initial charge, which means that the input of the inverter is low, and its output is high. C1 therefore charges via R1 until the voltage on C1 goes above the upper threshold level of the trigger. Its output then goes low, and C1 discharges into the output stage of the trigger by way of R1. This continues until the charge potential on C1 falls below the lower threshold voltage of the trigger circuit, at which point the output triggers to the high state. C1 then starts to charge-up via R1 again, and the circuit oscillates indefinitely with C1 being repeatedly charged and discharged. This gives a roughly triangular waveform across C1, but this signal is at a relatively high impedance and is not a proper TTL compatible type. The signal at the output of IC1 is a roughly squarewave type which is, of course, fully TTL compatible. Due to a slight lack of symmetry in IC1 the output signal has a mark-space ratio that is well removed from 1:1. In fact it is usually something in the region of 1:2.

Using the specified values the circuit operates at approximately 200Hz. In the interest of reliability it is advisable to leave R1 at 1k and set the output frequency by choosing the appropriate value for C1. The latter can have any value from a few picofarads upwards, and can be a large electrolytic type if necessary. Therefore, despite the low value of R1 it is still possible to achieve quite low output frequencies. In fact frequencies of less than 1Hz can be generated. The circuit will operate at frequencies of up to several megahertz, but a frequency of about 1MHz probably represents a practical upper limit.

This circuit will work using a 7414, but not with R1 at a value of 1k. A lower value is required, and 330R should be suitable. Reducing R1 by a factor of three means that C1 has to be three times higher in value for a given output frequency.

Crystal Oscillators

Many digital circuits require an accurate timing signal, and this is normally provided by an oscillator which has its operating frequency controlled by a quartz crystal. Crystal oscillators mainly operate at quite high frequencies, but they can be used in low frequency time bases if the output signal from the

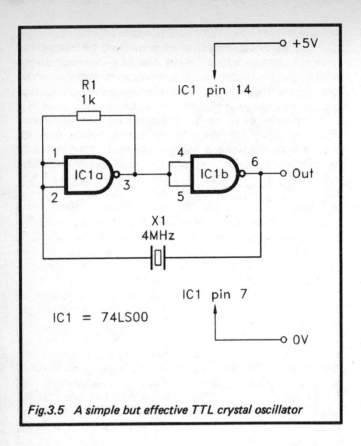

Fig.3.5 A simple but effective TTL crystal oscillator

oscillator is fed to a divider circuit. This topic is covered in a later section in this chapter.

For most purposes the simple crystal oscillator circuit of Figure 3.5 will suffice. IC1a is biased by R1, and it then acts as an amplifier in conjunction with IC1b. The input and output of the amplifier are in-phase, and crystal X1 therefore provides positive feedback. At the series resonant frequency of the crystal there will be sufficient feedback to produce oscillation.

It is only fair to point out that the quoted frequency on most crystals is the parallel resonant frequency, and not the series resonant type. The practical consequence of this is that the circuit will often oscillate a few hundred hertz above the marked frequency of the crystal. In many applications this will be of no real significance, since crystal oscillators are often used for their stability rather than because an exact frequency is required. Where operation at a precise frequency is needed it might be better to opt for a different oscillator configuration. Alternatively, adding a trimmer in parallel with the crystal (Figure 3.6) permits the output frequency to be "pulled" downwards, and should permit operation at the

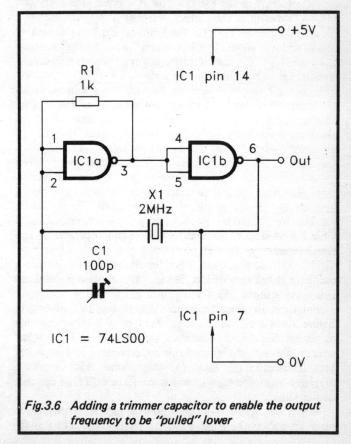

Fig.3.6 Adding a trimmer capacitor to enable the output frequency to be "pulled" lower

marked frequency. Be careful though, as too much capacitance will result in the operating frequency being taken well away from the crystal frequency. The trimmer capacitor becomes the timing capacitance in a C — R oscillator, and the crystal has no significant effect on the circuit.

The circuit will operate over a wide frequency range of at least 500kHz to 12MHz. In common with other simple crystal oscillator circuits, it is not suitable for use with overtone crystals. These are designed to operate at several times the fundamental frequency of the crystal, and many crystals for operation above about 8MHz are of this type. These crystals will only operate at the correct overtone if they are used in a circuit that has an L — C tuned circuit which is resonant at the overtone frequency. When used in an oscillator which lacks an L — C tuned circuit, an overtone crystal simply resonates at its fundamental frequency.

Figure 3.7 shows the circuit diagram for a simple crystal oscillator which uses a similar configuration to the trigger/inverter oscillator described previously. R1 and C1 set an operating frequency that is close to the resonant frequency of the crystal, but the crystal effectively takes over and holds the output signal at its parallel resonant frequency. The specified value for C1 is suitable for a 1MHz crystal, but it must be made proportionately lower in value for higher frequencies. For example, a value of about 39p should be suitable for a 4MHz crystal, but a little experimentation might be needed in order to obtain reliable operation. The circuit should work well at frequencies of up to at least 6MHz. One of the spare trigger/inverter circuits is used as a buffer at the output of the circuit. Another one provides an anti-phase output signal, but this is, of course, optional.

Many circuit designers prefer not to use TTL devices in crystal oscillators, and instead opt for a TTL compatible oscillator based on discrete components. The circuit diagram for an oscillator of this type appears in Figure 3.8. TR1 is used in the oscillator stage, while TR2 acts as a common emitter amplifier which provides a TTL compatible output signal.

The circuit will operate over quite a wide frequency range of about 500kHz to at least 6MHz. Ideally, the values of C1

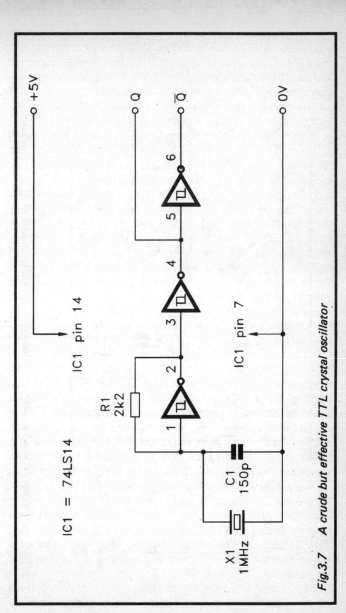

IC1 = 74LS14

+5V

IC1 pin 14

Q

Q̄

0V

IC1 pin 7

R1
2k2

C1
150p

X1
1MHz

Fig.3.7   A crude but effective TTL crystal oscillator

53

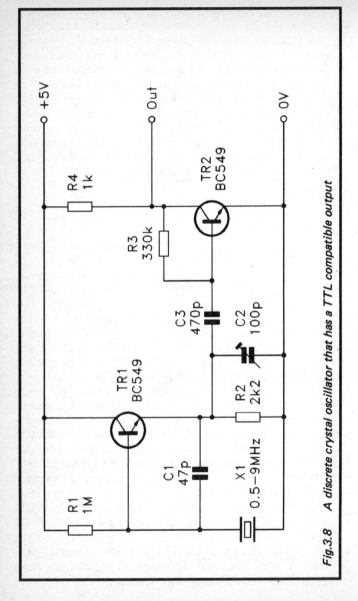

Fig.3.8   A discrete crystal oscillator that has a TTL compatible output

54

and C2 should be altered to suit the particular crystal frequency used. The values shown are well suited to operation at about 1MHz to 4MHz. At higher frequencies it is better to reduce C1 to about 22p, and C2 to a trimmer having a maximum capacitance of about 50p. The circuit should then work well using crystals having operating frequencies of around 4 to 10MHz. For crystals having operating frequencies of less than 1MHz it is advisable to increase C1 to a value of about 100p. Operation down to about 200kHz should then be possible. C2 enables the output frequency to be trimmed to precisely the correct frequency. If this facility is not required, replace C2 with a fixed capacitor having the same value as C1.

TTL VCO

The 74LS629 is one of the more unusual devices in the TTL range of devices. It is a dual voltage controlled oscillator (v.c.o.), and it was probably designed primarily for use in phase locked loops (p.l.l.s). However, it works well in more simple v.c.o. applications. It will operate at frequencies from the sub-audio through to a maximum of 20MHz. It has the unusual feature of possessing two sets of supply pins (pins 8 and 16, and 9 plus 15). These can be fed from a common 5 volt supply for operating frequencies up to 10MHz, but from 10MHz to 20MHz separate 5 volt supplies must be used. The total supply current is about 35 milliamps incidentally. Figure 3.9 shows the circuit diagram for a twin v.c.o. based on the 74LS629.

The only discrete timing component is C1 (and C2 in the second oscillator). This should be a non-polarised capacitor, although in non-critical applications where low frequency operation is needed it seems to be possible to use an electrolytic capacitor successfully. If an electrolytic capacitor should be used, its polarity is unimportant since there is no significant d.c. polarising voltage! The output frequency is inversely proportional to the value of C1.

With the "Range" input connected to the 0 volt supply rail and a control voltage of zero, the specified value for C1 gives an output frequency of about 2.5kHz. The output frequency rises to about 28kHz with a control voltage of 5 volts. As with practically all integrated circuits, the input voltage should not exceed the supply voltage.

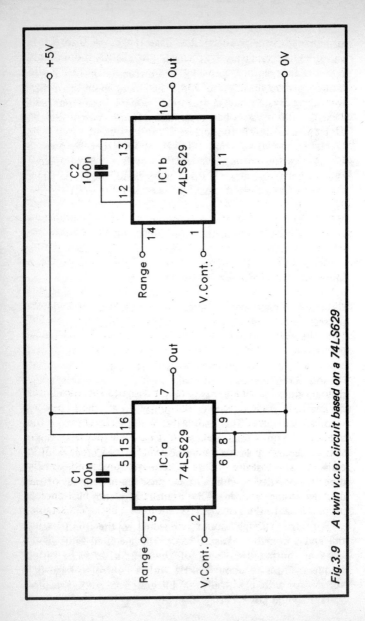

Fig.3.9 A twin v.c.o. circuit based on a 74LS629

The effect of the range input is to control the frequency span covered by a given input voltage range. A 0 to 5 volt control voltage range always seems to give slightly more than a 10 to 1 change in the output frequency. Increasing the voltage on the range input simply drags the frequency range lower. For example, the 2.5kHz to 28kHz frequency span mentioned previously can be brought down to a 550Hz to 6kHz span by increasing the voltage on the range input to 5 volts. When trying to achieve high output frequencies it is best to have a low voltage on the range input. When trying to achieve low output frequencies it is advantageous to have the range input at or close to the 5 volt supply potential. In some applications it could be useful to have a variable voltage supplied to the range input by a preset resistor connected across the supply rails. This would enable the output frequency range to be trimmed manually. In any event, getting a satisfactory output voltage range is likely to involve a certain amount of experimentation.

The linearity of the 74LS629 is quite good, but it is not suitable for use in applications that require very high degrees of linearity over a wide control voltage range. The output signal is a squarewave type having an accurate 1 to 1 mark-space ratio.

555 Oscillator

Although the 555 timer chips are not designed specifically for use in TTL logic circuits, the outputs of these devices actually have good compatibility with TTL chips. The standard device works well with TTL logic devices, as do most of the low power versions (ICM7555, L555, TLC555CP, etc.). As minute levels of current consumption are not usually of great importance with TTL circuits, the lower cost of the standard 555 means that it will normally be the best choice.

Figure 3.10 shows the configuration for a basic 555 astable, and the specified values for R1, R2, and C2 give an operating frequency of about 1kHz. There is insufficient space available here for a proper discussion of the 555, but it is worth bearing in mind that a 555 astable is often the best choice when a simple clock oscillator is needed for a TTL logic circuit. It is particularly useful when a very low operating frequency is

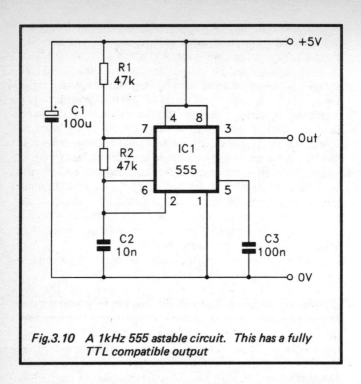

*Fig.3.10   A 1kHz 555 astable circuit.   This has a fully
TTL compatible output*

needed. The 555 can operate with high value timing components. Obtaining output frequencies of less than 1Hz is therefore easily achieved using a 555 oscillator, but this is not true
of simple TTL based C − R oscillators.

Signal Gate

Many applications require an oscillator signal that can be
switched on and off (gated) under the control of a logic
signal. With a lot of counter circuits, etc., there is no need
for any external gating circuitry, since they have built-in
gate circuits. The clock input signal is continuous, and is
effectively switched on or off by a logic signal fed to the
appropriate pin of the chip concerned.

   Where internal gating is not available, one approach to the
problem is to add an external signal gate. Figure 3.11 shows

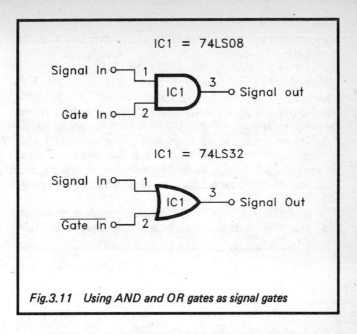

Fig.3.11 *Using AND and OR gates as signal gates*

two methods of achieving this. Using an AND gate gives
conventional ("true") gating, with a high control level result-
ing in the signal being passed through the output, and a low
control level blocking the signal. Using an OR gate gives the
opposite of this (complement gating), with a low control
level enabling the signal to pass through to the output, and a
high level blocking the signal.

It is possible to use a NAND gate instead of an AND
type, or a NOR type in place of an OR gate. However, NAND
and NOR gates give an inversion of the signal. This inversion
will be irrelevant in many cases, but might sometimes be of
significance.

Gated Astables
Another approach to the problem is to have an oscillator that
can be gated on and off. This method is obviously only
applicable in situations where it is an internally generated
clock signal that must be controlled. It is not usable if the

signal to be controlled is something like an external signal being applied to the input of a digital frequency meter circuit.

A basic TTL astable circuit is easily reconfigured to operate as a gated astable, but it must be the type made from gates rather than one based on a trigger/inverter. Figure 3.12 shows the circuit for a basic gated astable. The circuit is based on two 2 input NAND gates. One input of IC1a is used in the normal way, but the control signal is applied to the other input. This input is taken high in order to enable oscillation. Note that the output goes low when oscillation is blocked. An inverter should be added at the output if it is important that the output should be high under standby conditions.

The circuit of Figure 3.13 is basically the same as the one just described, but it is based on NOR gates rather than

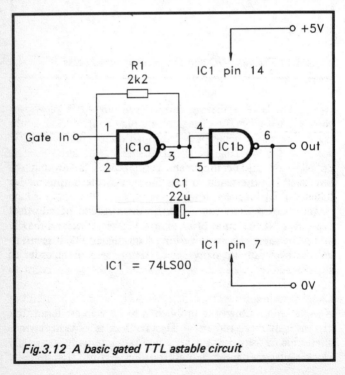

Fig.3.12 A basic gated TTL astable circuit

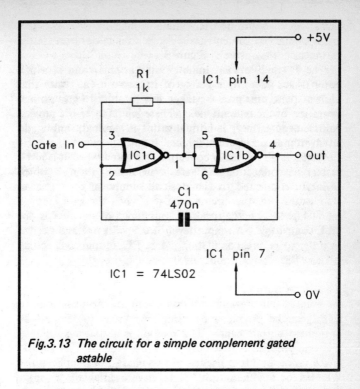

Fig.3.13 The circuit for a simple complement gated astable

NAND types. The practical importance of this is that the circuit provides complement gating (i.e. oscillation is enabled when the gate signal is low). The output of this circuit is high under standby conditions. An inverter should be added at the output if the input must be low when oscillation is blocked. Note that with this version of the gated astable it seems to be necessary to use a low value timing resistor in order to obtain oscillation. Values from about 470R to 1k seem to give satisfactory results.

It is possible to gate the crystal controlled astable circuit of Figure 3.5 by using one input of IC1a as the gate input, but this will often fail to give satisfactory results. The problem is that a circuit of this type will often take a short (but possibly significant time) to start oscillating properly. Also, initially there can be spurious oscillations at high frequencies. If a gated crystal oscillator is needed it is safer to opt for external gating, as in the circuit of Figure 3.14.

The 74LS629 has an "inhibit" input at pins 6 and 11 which can be used to provide gating of its two v.c.o.s. Note that each of these pins must be taken low in order to give normal operation of the relevant v.c.o. These inputs therefore provide complement gating. If normal gating is required, simply add an inverter ahead of each "inhibit" input.

A 555 astable is easily converted to a gated type. It is just a matter of connecting the gate input signal to pin 4 (which formerly connected to the positive supply rail). This gives true gating (i.e. the circuit oscillates when the gate input is taken high). Strictly speaking, this input of the 555 is not TTL compatible. An input level of 0.5 volts or less is needed in order to suppress oscillation. Most TTL outputs will actual-ly drive this input without any difficulties though.

Two-Phase Outputs

As pointed out previously, a crude form of two-phase output signal can be produced by using an inverter to generate an anti-phase output signal. This method is not always suitable, and one problem is that outputs having accurate 1 to 1 mark-space ratios are often needed in two-phase clock applications. Whether or not the output signals have a suitable mark-space ratio is dependent on the design of the oscillator, but in many cases the mark-space ratio will not be accurate enough.

The second problem is that an inverter is something less than instant. A transition at its input does not result in an opposite transition immediately appearing on its output. There is a propagation delay through the circuit, which is something that occurs with all logic circuits incidentally. For a simple device such as an inverter the propagation delay will be very short indeed. For example, the propagation delay for each section of a 74LS14 is a mere 15ns. However, this can still be of significance in some applications, particularly where high clock frequencies are used.

The standard method of obtaining a really accurate two-phase clock signal is to feed the output of the clock oscillator into a flip/flop connected to operate as a divide by two circuit.

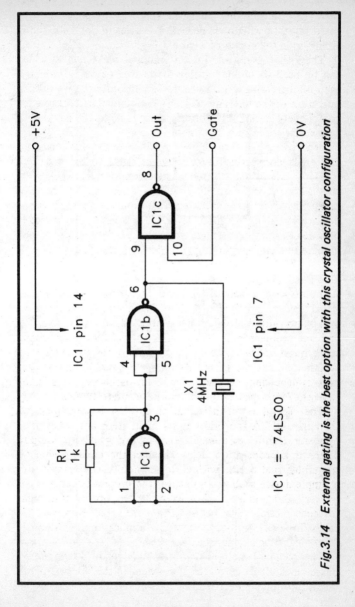

Fig. 3.14 External gating is the best option with this crystal oscillator configuration

63

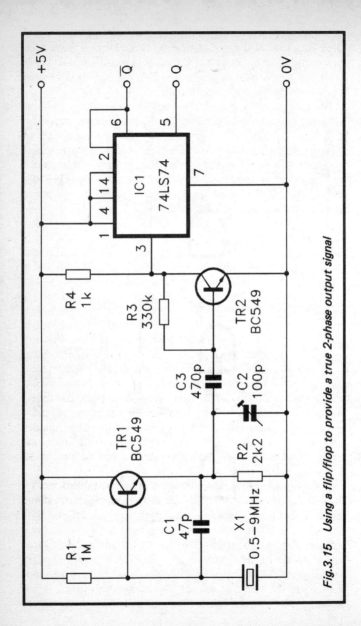

Fig.3.15 Using a flip/flop to provide a true 2-phase output signal

64

Flip/flops are covered in Chapter 4, and their operation is not something that will be discussed in detail here. Figure 3.15 shows the circuit diagram for a two-phase crystal clock oscillator which uses one section of a 74LS74 dual D type flip/flop as the divide by two circuit.

Feeding any TTL compatible oscillator signal into pin 3 of IC1 will produce a high quality two-phase output signal on pins 5 and 6. The two outputs will switch in unison, and an accurate 1 to 1 mark-space ratio will be produced regardless of the input signal's mark-space ratio. Remember that the circuit provides a divide by two action as well as generating two-phase output signals. The clock oscillator must therefore operate at double the required clock frequency.

Monostables

A monostable is an electronic timing circuit which is triggered by an input pulse, and then provides an output pulse of a certain duration. In virtually all practical monostable circuits the output pulse duration is controlled by a $C - R$ timing network. Monostables are used where it is important to have a pulse of a certain duration, and the length of the input pulses is not suitable. In many applications pulses of fixed duration must be produced from trigger pulses of varying lengths.

Monostables are used in what are essentially pulse stretching and pulse shortening applications. It is important to realise that some monostables can act as both pulse shorteners and pulse stretchers, while others will only function properly as pulse stretchers. It is the so-called "retriggerable" monostables that can only operate as pulse stretchers. Using a long input pulse with a retriggerable monostable results in an elongated output pulse.

Probably the best known of the TTL monostable devices is the 74121. Note that this only seems to be available in a standard TTL version. I have not encountered an LS, HC, or HCT version of this particular chip. Triggering a 74121 is something less than straightforward due to the inclusion of some gating ahead of its trigger input. The latter is not directly accessible, and triggering has to be accomplished via the input gating. In the vast majority of applications this gating is not required, but it is not difficult to rationalise things to produce simple positive and negative edge triggered monostables.

Figure 3.16 shows the circuit diagram for a simple monostable which is based on the 74121. This is a positive edge triggered monostable, which simply means that the output pulse commences as the input is taken through a low to high transition. Figure 3.17 shows the circuit for a negative edge triggered monostable. This is triggered by a high to low transition on the input. The positive triggered circuit has a Schmitt trigger input stage which ensures that it will trigger reliably from slow input signals. The negative triggered circuit lacks this facility, and must be driven by normal TTL pulses.

In both cases the output goes high for a duration that is controlled by the values of C1 and R1. The pulse duration is approximately equal to 0.695 C R seconds, which works

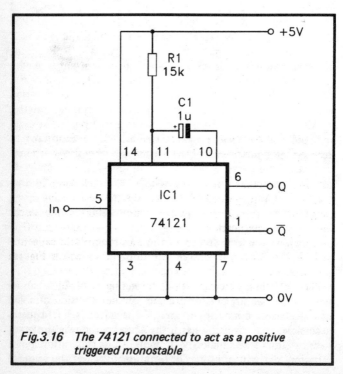

Fig.3.16   The 74121 connected to act as a positive triggered monostable

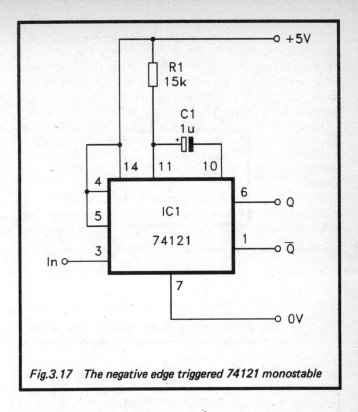

Fig.3.17 The negative edge triggered 74121 monostable

out at about 10ms using the example values. R1 should have a value in the range 1k4 to 40k. C1 should have a value in the range 10p to 10μ. Higher values of up to 1000μ can be used, but only in applications where a very rapid pulse cutoff is not essential. It is acceptable to use an electrolytic capacitor provided it is connected with the polarity shown in Figures 3.16 and 3.17.

The 74121 has an internal 2k timing resistor which can be used by connecting pin 9 to the +5 volt supply rail, as in the positive triggered monostable circuit of Figure 3.18. Of course, if the internal timing resistor is used, no discrete timing resistor should be connected to pin 11. A very short pulse duration of about 30ns can be obtained by using the internal

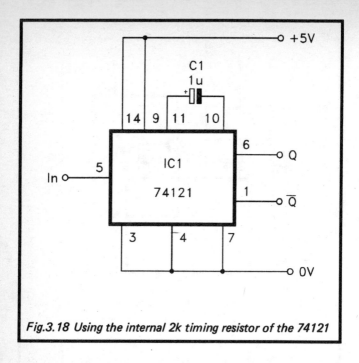

Fig.3.18 Using the internal 2k timing resistor of the 74121

timing resistor and omitting the external timing capacitor (C1). 74121 monostables are not retriggerable types, and they are therefore capable of operating as both pulse shorteners and pulse stretchers.

The 74LS123 and 74LS221 are very useful dual monostables. The main difference between the two is that the 74LS123 has normal TTL inputs, while those of the 74LS221 are Schmitt trigger types. The 74LS221 is therefore the better choice if the trigger signal might be a slow switching type. These devices have negative and positive trigger inputs, and can be used in either mode. Figure 3.19 shows the positive triggered monostable configurations. The left-hand circuit has section 1 of the device in the standard mode with a non-polarised timing capacitor. The right-hand circuit utilizes section 2 of the device in a circuit which incorporates a polarised timing capacitor. This necessitates the addition of a

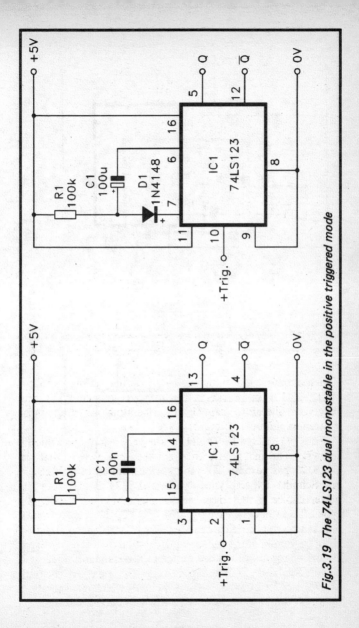

Fig.3.19 The 74LS123 dual monostable in the positive triggered mode

69

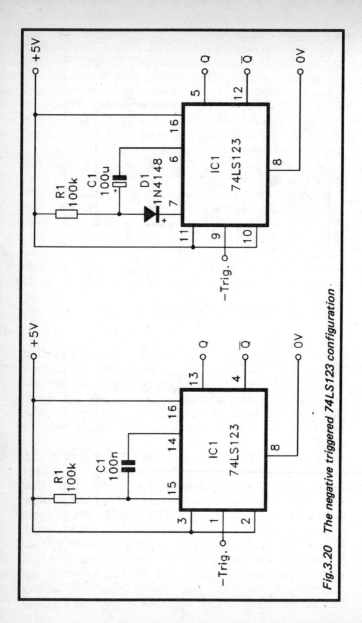

Fig.3.20 The negative triggered 74LS123 configuration

70

diode to the timing network.

R1 can be in the range 5k to 260k for the LS versions of these chips, or 5k to 50k for the standard TTL types. Any capacitance values can be used, but pulse durations become difficult to predict accurately for values under 1n. It is probably best to regard 100p as a practical minimum value. The output pulse duration is approximately 0.4 C R seconds (0.6 C R seconds for the 74LS221). This works out at about 4ms for the left-hand circuit, and 4 seconds for the right-hand circuit.

Figure 3.20 shows the negative edge triggered equivalents to the circuits of Figure 3.19. It is possible to use both inputs of each monostable if required. It is a combination of the positive inputs (pins 2 and 10) being in the high state, and the negative inputs (pins 1 and 9) being in the low state that causes triggering. These monostables are non-retriggerable types incidentally. Negative active reset inputs are available at pins 3 and 11. These are normally just held in the high state so that they have no effect. However, pulsing one of these inputs low results in the timing period of the relevant monostable being brought to an immediate end.

555 Monostable

As pointed out previously, the 555 timer chip works well in TTL circuits. This device can operate as both an oscillator and a monostable. This is not the place for a detailed discussion of the 555, but Figure 3.21 shows the circuit diagram for a basic 555 monostable. The output pulse duration is 1.1 R1 C2 seconds, or 1.1 seconds with the specified values.

The 555 is useful for applications that require a TTL compatible monostable which can produce long output pulses. The TTL monostable chips are less than ideal where long output pulses are needed due to their inability to operate with high timing resistor values. The 555 can operate with timing resistances of up to 20M, which means that pulse durations of more than one minute can be achieved quite easily. Bear in mind though, that high value timing resistors are only a practical proposition if the timing capacitor is a high quality type which has very low leakage levels. Timing capacitors of inadequate quality

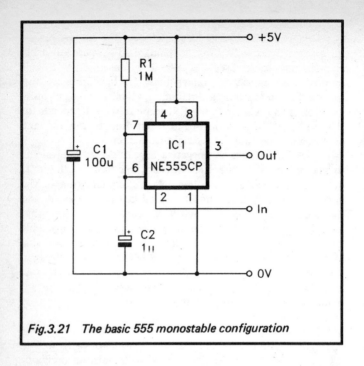

Fig.3.21 The basic 555 monostable configuration

will produce elongated and inconsistent pulse times. In an extreme case the output pulse will continue indefinitely.

A 555 monostable is a retriggerable type incidentally, and as such it can not act as a pulse shortener. However, in a TTL context it will mainly be used when long output pulses are needed, and it will not usually be required to provide pulse shortening. If necessary though, a 555 monostable can be preceded by (say) a 74121 pulse shortener to ensure that it provides output pulses of the correct duration.

Practical Circuits

Connecting one logic block to the next in a circuit does not usually produce any problems. This is one respect in which designing logic circuits is very much easier than designing analogue circuits (which tend to give frequent incompatibility problems between one stage and the next). Provided logic circuits are produced using devices which all come from the same logic family, and high levels of fanout are not used, every output is more or less guaranteed to correctly drive any inputs that are connected to it.

The only likely cause of problems is where a circuit has the logic devices operating close to their maximum permissible operating frequencies. In these circumstances it is as well to bear in mind that, in general, the more simple devices can operate at much higher frequencies than the more complex types. When designing TTL logic circuits that handle high frequencies it is therefore necessary to take great care that nothing in the circuit is used beyond its maximum frequency rating. Incidentally, it is extremely unlikely that any damage will occur if the maximum frequency rating of any TTL logic device is exceeded. The circuit will probably work perfectly well if the maximum frequency rating is only marginally exceeded. Trying to use devices well beyond their maximum frequency rating is almost certain to result in them failing to operate at all.

Connecting logic circuits to the outside world can be a slightly more difficult prospect, although in most cases this entails nothing more than driving a l.e.d., a loudspeaker, or something of this nature. Interfacing logic devices to simple components of these types is very straightforward. To complete this chapter we will consider a few practical circuits which demonstrate some simple logic interfacing techniques, as well as being useful circuits in their own rights. These circuits also demonstrate some ways in which astable and monostable circuits can be utilized in practical circuits.

Pulsed Tone Generators

The circuit of Figure 3.22 is for a pulsed tone generator, suitable for use as an audible alarm generator in applications which do not require very high volume levels. IC1c and IC1d operate as a gated astable which feeds a roughly squarewave signal at about 1kHz into loudspeaker LS1. A standard TTL or LS TTL output is only able to drive a few milliamps through a loudspeaker, which is not enough to give more than a very quiet tone. TR1 is therefore used as a common emitter switching stage which substantially boosts the maximum

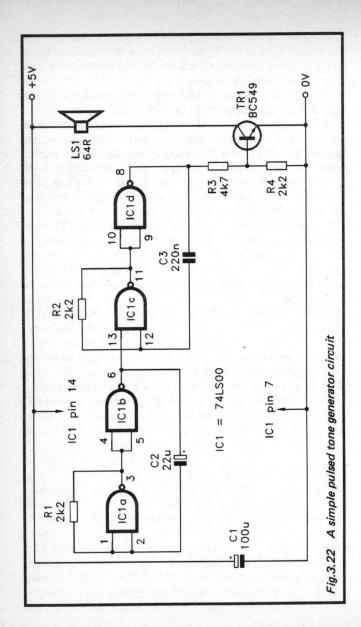

Fig.3.22 A simple pulsed tone generator circuit

74

available output current. In fact the output current available from TR1 is potentially more than its maximum collector current rating. The impedance of the load (LS1 in this case) must be high enough to ensure that the output current never exceeds 100 milliamps. Accordingly, LS1 should not have an impedance of less than about 50 ohms.

A tone that is modulated in some way gives a better alarm signal than one which simply sounds continuously and unchanged. The most simple form of modulation, and the one used here, is to switch the tone on and off at a rate of a few hertz. This is achieved here by using IC1a and IC1b as a low frequency oscillator which provides the gate signal for the tone generator astable.

An important point to note here is that when the tone generator is gated off, its output goes low. This produces a very low current flow through TR1 and LS1 when the tone generator is not operating. If the output of the tone generator went high when it was gated off, the circuit would still operate properly, but the current consumption would be greatly increased. Also, a strong current would be fed through LS1 during the periods of non-oscillation, which might not do it a great deal of good! If an oscillator is gated off for long periods of time it is definitely not acceptable for a high current to be fed through the loudspeaker during these periods.

The circuit of Figure 3.23 is for a high power version of the pulsed tone generator. This is much the same as the original, but TR1 has been changed to a Darlington power device. This has an extremely high current gain, which enables LS1 to be pulsed with a current of well over one amp. In order to give this much higher drive current the impedance of LS1 has been reduced to 8 ohms, and the supply voltage to the output stage has been increased to 12 volts. The main circuit must, of course, be powered from the usual 5 volt supply. This could be derived from the 12 volt supply via a 5 volt monolithic voltage regulator if necessary.

The 12 volt supply has a large decoupling capacitor (C4) so that it can deliver the large current pulses to LS1. The average current consumption from the 12 volt supply is under 1 amp. As TR1 is used in what is effectively a switching mode it does not dissipate much power, despite the fact that it is

75

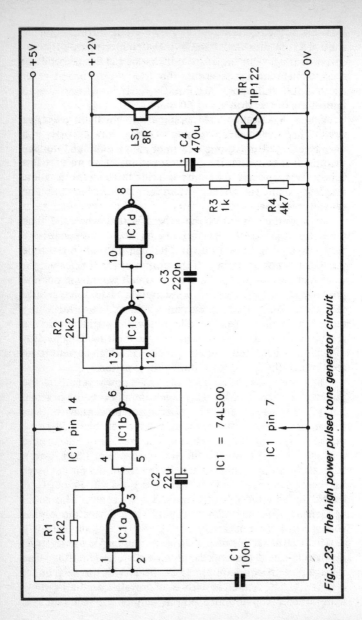

Fig.3.23 The high power pulsed tone generator circuit

76

handling quite high currents. However, it might require a small heatsink in order to ensure that there is absolutely no risk of it overheating. LS1 must be a type capable of handling powers of around 8 watts r.m.s. or more.

F.M. Alarm Generator
Ceramic resonators are now popular for use in alarm generator circuits. Although these components only draw currents of a few milliamps from the drive circuit, they can still produce quite high volume levels. They are suitable for many alarm applications, but are particularly well suited to those where small size and light weight are important. Due to their low drive current requirements they can be driven direct from standard TTL and LS TTL outputs. The volume level will be something less than earsplitting, due to the low output voltage swing from a TTL output. The volume is still adequate for many simple alarm applications though.

The circuit diagram for a simple modulated tone generator is shown in Figure 3.24. There is no need to worry about high currents flowing through a ceramic resonator under stand-by conditions, since the resistance through one of these components is many megohms. In fact a ceramic resonator "looks" to the driver circuit very much like a capacitor of a few nanofarads in value. When used with low voltage driver circuits they are sometimes connected across anti-phase outputs. In theory, this gives a peak to peak voltage swing across the resonator that is almost twice the supply voltage. In practice the loading on the outputs seems to be so heavy that the voltage swing is very much less than this. The volume level obtained seems to be little more than that provided by a single-ended driver circuit. Consequently a two-phase driver circuit is probably only a worthwhile proposition if it is essential to obtain the highest possible volume level.

There is a slight problem with ceramic resonators in that they offer high efficiency, but only over certain narrowly defined frequency bands. If a ceramic resonator is used with a single frequency tone generator circuit it is important that the pitch of the tone should be adjustable. It can then be set at a frequency where the resonator provides good efficiency, and produces a loud tone. Another approach to the problem,

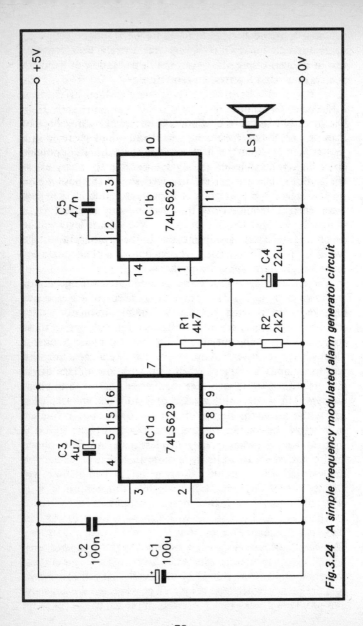

Fig.3.24 A simple frequency modulated alarm generator circuit

78

and the one used here, is to use a frequency modulated tone generator. Sweeping the output over a fairly wide range of audio frequencies ensures that the resonator is driven with frequencies which provide high efficiency. For part of the time it will also be driven at frequencies which offer lower efficiencies. This does not seem to detract significantly from the effectiveness of the alarm signal though. This type of alarm signal is a very effective one which is not easily missed.

IC1 is a 74LS629 dual v.c.o. which is used here to provide both the audio tone and the modulation signal. IC1a acts as the low frequency oscillator which generates the modulation signal, while IC1b operate as the tone generator. The output from IC1a is coupled to the control input of IC1b via a potential divider circuit (R1–R2). This reduces the sweep range to one that is appropriate to this application. C4 smooths the modulation signal, converting it from a square-wave type to something more like a triangular waveform. This gives an output signal that is swept upwards and down-ward in frequency, rather than simply switching between two frequencies. The result is a very effective alarm sound.

Figure 3.25 shows the circuit diagram for a modulated tone generator that is a variation on the circuit of Figure 3.24. C4 has been omitted so that the audio tone is simply switched between two tones, giving a sort of warbling sound. Some may prefer this to the swept audio tone, and both types of signal are very effective in alarm applications. This circuit has a simple common emitter output stage which drives an ordinary high impedance moving coil loudspeaker. This is preferable to a ceramic resonator, which might not offer good efficiencies at the particular tones produced by the circuit. The current consumption of this circuit is much higher than that of the original, although it will probably provide a some-what higher volume level.

Analogue Frequency Meter
Figure 3.26 shows the circuit diagram for a three range ana-logue frequency meter. The circuit breaks down into three main sections. In the first of these IC1 is used in a simple non-inverting amplifier circuit which has an approximate closed loop voltage gain of 69 times. This amplifies the input

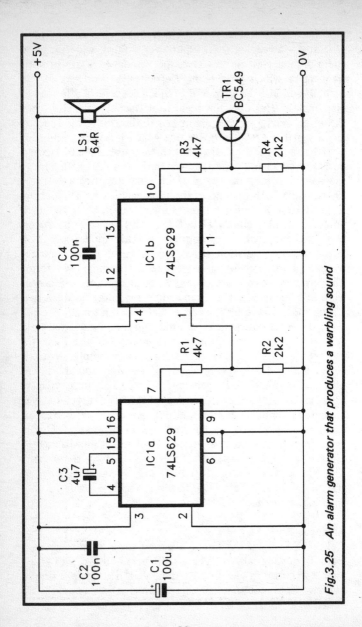

Fig.3.25   An alarm generator that produces a warbling sound

80

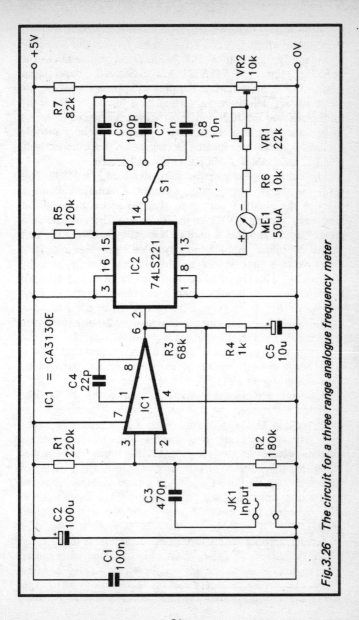

Fig.3.26 The circuit for a three range analogue frequency meter

81

signal to a level that can reliably operate the second stage of the circuit, which is a non-retriggerable monostable based on IC2. In this application the 74LS221 is preferable to the 74LS123, since the 74LS221 has a Schmitt trigger input stage. This is important in the present application where the input voltage will often vary at quite a low rate. R5 is the timing resistor for IC2, and the timing capacitance is one of three capacitors selected via S1. These capacitors provide the unit with its three measuring ranges. C8 to C6 respectively give full scale values of 500Hz, 5kHz, and 50kHz.

The third stage is a simple voltmeter based on ME1. This reads the average output voltage from the monostable, but in practice the circuit is set up so that the meter gives a direct frequency reading. VR1 controls the sensitivity of the voltmeter circuit, and this is used to accurately calibrate the unit against a known input frequency. VR2 provides a variable offset voltage that is used to null the meter under standby conditions. This is needed because the output of IC2 does not go right down to 0 volts when it is in the low state. If the output of IC2 is at (say) 0.2 volts when in the low state, adjusting VR2 for a wiper potential of 0.2 volts gives zero volts across the meter under standby conditions. In order to obtain good accuracy on all ranges it is important that C6, C7, and C8 are close tolerance components. Ideally they should have a tolerance of 1%.

Although a monostable may not seem to be the obvious basis for a frequency to voltage converter, it actually works quite well in this application. With a low input frequency the output pulses are well spaced out, and the average output voltage is very low. As the input frequency is increased, the number of output pulses in a given period of time increases, as does the average output voltage. Provided the input frequency is not excessive, there is a linear relationship between the input frequency and the average output voltage.

Simply feeding an analogue device such as a moving coil voltmeter direct with the digital output of the main circuit may at first seem to be an unsatisfactory way of handling things. However, the meter can not follow the rapid changes in the output voltage from the monostable, and instead simply responds to the average output voltage. Since this is exactly what is required, there is no point in adding any smoothing circuits or other interface circuitry at the output of the monostable. Unfortunately, there are few other analogue components which will interface to a digital circuit as easily as this!

An accurate reference frequency is needed in order to calibrate the unit, and ideally this frequency should be equal to the full scale value of one range. This could perhaps be a 50kHz signal provided by a crystal calibrator. The unit is reasonably sensitive, and an input level of as little as 10 millivolts r.m.s. will probably drive the circuit properly. Start with VR1 at maximum resistance, and the wiper of VR2 at the 0 volt end of its track. The meter should show a small positive deflection at switch-on, and by adjusting VR2 it should be possible to zero the meter. Then set S1 to the appropriate range, connect the calibration signal, and adjust VR1 for the correct meter reading. It is advisable to repeat the adjustment of VR1 and VR2 to ensure that everything is spot-on.

The meter's 0 to 50 scaling is obviously correct for the 50kHz range. Additional scales can be marked for the other ranges, but it is probably not worthwhile doing this. A little mental arithmetic is all that is needed in order to shift the decimal place into the correct position when taking readings.

One final point is that this circuit must be powered from a well stabilised 5 volt supply. Any variations in the supply voltage will produce similar variations in the accuracy of the unit. TTL circuits are normally powered from well stabilised supplies anyway, but with this circuit it is definitely not acceptable to use something like a 5 volt NiCad battery supply.

Logic Probe

The circuit of Figure 3.27 is for a simple logic probe for use with TTL digital circuits (or circuits which use TTL compatible devices). It is not suitable for use with circuits that are based on 4000 series CMOS integrated circuits. The circuit uses three l.e.d.s to show the state present at the test point. IC1a is used as an inverter at the input of the probe, and this

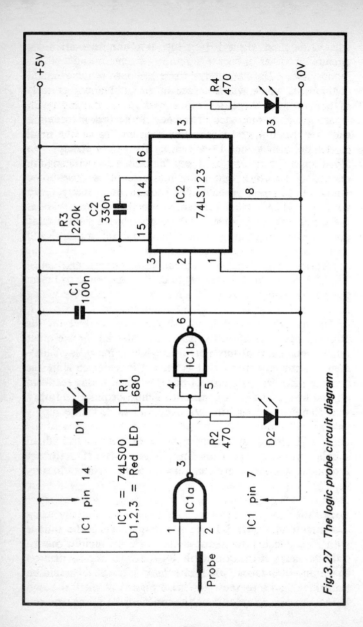

Fig.3.27 The logic probe circuit diagram

84

drives two l.e.d. indicators. A static low input level results in D2 switching on, while a static high level results in D1 being activated.

A pulsing test point causes both l.e.d.s to switch on, and their relative brightness is dependent on the mark-space ratio of the test signal. With an extreme mark-space ratio and a high input frequency only one of the l.e.d.s will appear to switch on. The other l.e.d. will be switched on for such a small percentage of the time that it will fail to glow visibly. An illegal input voltage can also result in both l.e.d.s switching on. For the unit to be really useful it is essential to have some means of determining whether the test point is genuinely static or if there are occasional and very brief pulses present. It is also necessary to have some means of distinguishing between a pulsing test point and one which is not at a valid logic level.

IC2 is a monostable formed from one section of a 74LS123. R3 and C2 are the timing components, and they produce an output pulse duration of about 30ms. This is long enough to give a very noticeable flash from l.e.d. indicator D3, which is driven from the Q output of the monostable. IC2 is triggered by the input signal, and it provides a pulse stretcher action. An input pulse of less than a microsecond will produce a flash from D3. A flash from D3 therefore indicates that the test point is pulsing, even if this is not apparent from D1 and D2. If the test point is pulsing briefly and very infrequently, each individual pulse will be indicated by a flash from D3.

The circuit is very simple, and there should be little difficulty in fitting it into a small probe type case. The current consumption of the circuit is not very high, and it can therefore be powered from the circuit under test. This table summarises the results obtained from various types of input signal, and this should make life easier when initially using the unit. Note that D3 will often flash when the unit is initially connected to a test point. This is simply due to spurious input pulses generated when making the connection to the test point, and any initial flashing from D3 should be ignored. When the input is left floating it will go to the high state. Therefore, under standby conditions D1 is switched on, and D2 plus D3 are switched off.

Input State	D1	D2	D3
Static Low	Off	On	Off
Static High	On	Off	Off
Invalid Voltage	On	On	Off
Pulsing (1:1 approx.)	On	On	Flashing
Brief High Pulses	Off	On	Flashing
Brief Low Pulses	On	Off	Flashing
No Input	On	Off	Off

Chapter 4

FLIP/FLOPS AND DIVIDERS

Flip/flops are used in a variety of applications, but are mainly used in the control logic sections of digital circuits. Dividers are mainly used where a highly accurate low frequency clock signal is required. The standard method of producing such a signal is to start with a high frequency signal generated by a crystal oscillator, and to then feed the signal through a chain of divider circuits which, ultimately, produce the required low frequency signal. Dividers can also be used in control logic circuits where simple flip/flops are inadequate to handle things properly.

Basic Flip/Flops

The most basic form of flip/flop is the set/reset type, which is often referred to as an "S/R" flip/flop. An S/R flip/flop can be produced from a couple of 2 input NOR or NAND gates, as shown in Figures 4.1 and 4.2 respectively. For the circuit of Figure 4.1 a positive pulse at the "set" input takes the Q output high, and the not Q output low. A positive pulse at the "reset" input then takes the Q output low and the not Q output high. Another positive pulse to the "set" input takes the Q output high again, and so on. The circuit of Figure 4.2 has negative active inputs. Accordingly, a negative pulse to the "set" input takes the Q output high, and a negative pulse to the "reset" input returns the Q output to the low state.

Once an S/R flip/flop has been set, further input pulses to the "set" input have no effect until it has been reset. Similarly, when in the reset state, reset pulses have no effect. With a basic S/R flip/flop it is important that the two inputs are not fed with positive pulses simultaneously, as this would give unpredictable results.

Figure 4.3 shows the circuit diagram for a manually controlled S/R flip/flop. Pressing S1 sets the Q output high — pressing S2 resets it to the low state. A typical application would be as a sort of on/off switch for some function of the

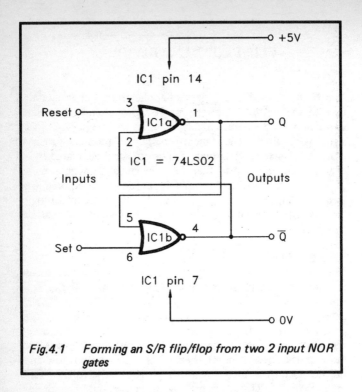

Fig.4.1   Forming an S/R flip/flop from two 2 input NOR
gates

main circuit. Pressing S1 would switch on the main circuit, or
possibly some function in a complex unit. Pressing S2 would
switch the main circuit or function off again.

"D" Type Flip/Flop

A "D" (data) type flip/flop is rather more complex than an
S/R type, but it is still one of the more basic types of flip/
flop. Figure 4.4(a) shows the inputs (left) and outputs (right)
of a "D" type flip/flop. It is only fair to point out that many
practical "D" type flip/flops do not have a full set of inputs
and outputs. In particular, the "set" input and the not Q
output are often absent.

A "D" type flip/flop can be used in a number of ways. A
positive pulse to the set input takes the Q output high and the

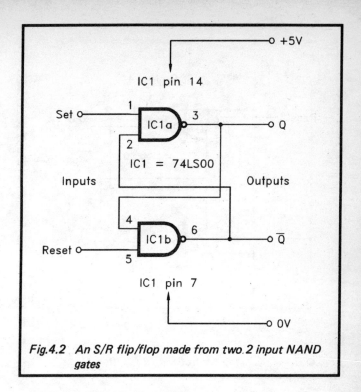

Fig.4.2 An S/R flip/flop made from two 2 input NAND gates

not Q output low. A positive pulse to the "reset" input takes the Q output low and the not Q output high. A "D" type flip/flop can therefore act as a simple S/R type if desired. However, a "D" type flip/flop is not often used in this manner. The "set" and "reset" inputs are mainly used to take the outputs to the required initial states, although they may be needed at other times to force the outputs to the required states. In many applications these inputs are not required at all, and they are then simply connected to the 0 volt supply rail.

One application of a "D" type flip/flop is as a simple memory cell. This type of circuit is known as a "data latch". The logic state to be "remembered" is fed to the "data" input. A pulse is then fed to the "clock" input, and this

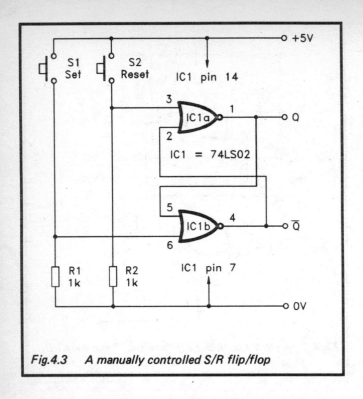

Fig.4.3   A manually controlled S/R flip/flop

latches the input state on the Q output. Changing the logic level at the "data" input then has no affect on the Q output. The "remembered" logic level will be held on the Q output until another clock pulse is received. The Q output will then take up whatever logic level happens to be present at the "data" input during the trailing edge of the clock pulse. Of course, the Q output can be forced to any desired state at any time using the "set" and "reset" inputs, which always have the ability to override the other two inputs.

Data latches are quite common in digital circuits, where the required data is often only present for a few microseconds or less. A data latch, plus a control logic circuit which provides the latching pulses to the "clock" input, provides a means of grabbing the intermittent pieces of data

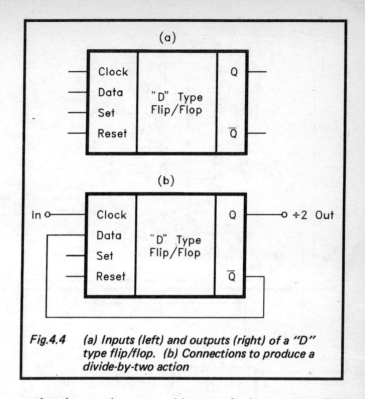

Fig.4.4   (a) Inputs (left) and outputs (right) of a "D"
         type flip/flop. (b) Connections to produce a
         divide-by-two action

so that they can be processed by some further circuitry. This is a subject we will return to in Chapter 5.

A "D" type flip/flop can be used as a divide by two circuit if it is connected in the manner shown in Figure 4.4(b). The stream of input pulses are applied to the "clock" input, and the not Q output is coupled back to the "data" input. Suppose that the not Q output is high. On the next input pulse the "data" input will be fed with this high logic level, which will take the Q output high and the not Q output low. On the next clock input pulse the "data" input will be fed with the low output level from the not Q output. This latches the Q output low and the not Q output high. Thus, on each input pulse the outputs change state. Two input pulses are therefore needed to give one full output pulse (two transitions),

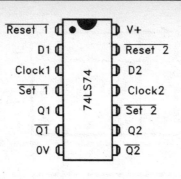

Fig.4.5 Pinout details for the 74LS74 dual "D" type flip/flop

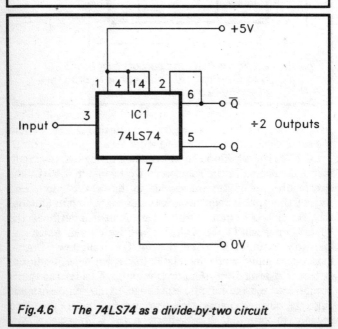

Fig.4.6 The 74LS74 as a divide-by-two circuit

92

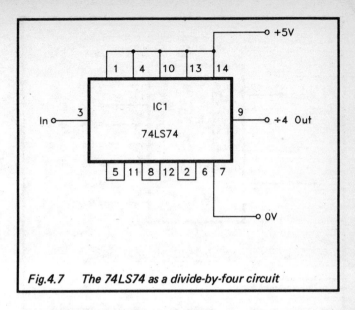

Fig.4.7   The 74LS74 as a divide-by-four circuit

and a divide by two action is obtained.

The 74LS74 is a dual "D" type flip/flop, and it has the pinout configuration shown in Figure 4.5. This can operate as a divide by two circuit using the method of connection shown in Figure 4.6. In the circuit of Figure 4.7 the two flip/flops are connected to operate as divide by two circuits, but they are wired in series so that a divide by four action is produced. The 74LS74 can operate with input frequencies of up to 33MHz, and the 7474 can handle a maximum input frequency of 25MHz. The equivalent figures for the HC and ALS versions are 40MHz and 50MHz respectively. The maximum input frequency for the AC version is an impressive 125MHz.

Ripple Counters

A long chain of divide by two circuits could be produced using single or dual flip/flop devices, but it is easier and more economic to use the various multi-stage divider chips that are available. These are normally referred to as "ripple" counters or "binary" counters. Unfortunately, the TTL range is not

93

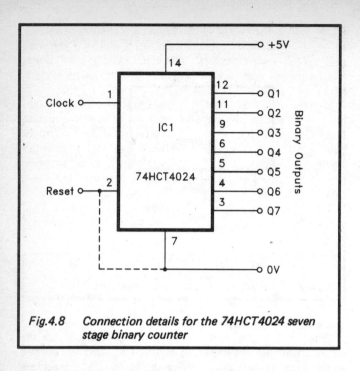

Fig.4.8   Connection details for the 74HCT4024 seven
stage binary counter

exactly "brimming over" with long binary counters. There
are no widely available TTL devices of this type. Rather
than building up long dividers the "hard way" it is probably best to resort to CMOS divider chips in their HC or HCT
versions. The 4024BE is the most simple of the CMOS ripple
counters, and it is a seven stage type. It is produced in both
HC and HCT versions, but the HCT version is less widely
available. The 74HC4024 can operate with input frequencies
of up to 70MHz. Figure 4.8 shows the basic way in which
this device is used.

The input pulses are applied to the "clock" input, and the
only other input is the "reset" terminal. Ripple counters
normally have just these two inputs. Pulsing the reset input
high results in all the outputs being taken low. In many
divider applications the reset input is not required, and it is
then simply connected to the 0 volt supply rail. It is important

to remember that many TTL devices require negative reset pulses, whereas CMOS types (including HC and HCT versions) require positive reset signals. With some circuits it will therefore be necessary to invert the reset signal before applying it to the CMOS divider circuit.

Sometimes it is necessary to provide a reset pulse at switch-on, but thereafter the counter must be allowed to operate normally. In such cases a C − R network across the supply rails can be used to generate an initial reset pulse, as in the circuit of Figure 4.9. This method should work properly using any CMOS devices which need a positive reset pulse at switch-on.

On the output side of the device there are the seven Q outputs, which are simply numbered "1" to "7". These are

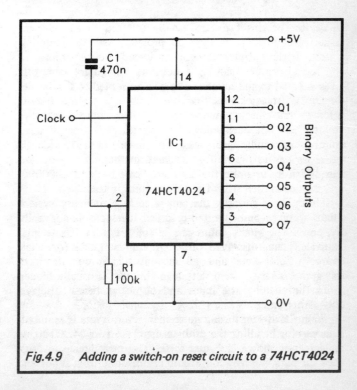

Fig.4.9   Adding a switch-on reset circuit to a 74HCT4024

simply the outputs of divider stages one to seven respectively. Ripple counters do not normally have complementary not Q outputs, but these can, if necessary, be produced by feeding each Q output through an inverter stage. The division rates at each output are as follows:

Output	Division Rate
Q1	2
Q2	4
Q3	8
Q4	16
Q5	32
Q6	64
Q7	128

Devices of this type are usually referred to as counters rather than dividers as they do provide a sort of counting action. If the output states are considered in terms of logic 1s and logic 0s rather than highs and lows, the binary value this gives is equal to the number of clock pulses fed to the device. Of course, this assumes that the counter was reset to zero prior to the count commencing. It also assumes that the counter has not been allowed to overflow. A seven stage counter can handle binary values of up to 1111111, which is equal to 127 in the normal decimal numbering system. On the 128th input pulse the counter cycles back to 0000000, and the count then starts from the beginning again.

Although a counter that operates in the binary system might seem to be of limited practical value, this is not really the case. The binary count can be converted into its decimal equivalent and displayed on seven segment l.e.d.s (or whatever). Computers and all current digital circuits work using the binary system, although this fact is usually hidden from the user by the input and output methods (displays, keyboards, etc.).

Where a divider having more than seven stages is required, one way of handling the problem is to use two 74HCT4024s in series, as shown in Figure 4.10. This provides up to fourteen outputs, but by adding more devices in series it is possible

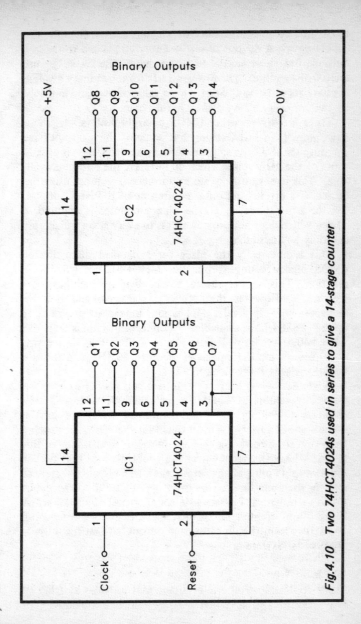

Fig.4.10   Two 74HCT4024s used in series to give a 14-stage counter

97

to obtain any number of outputs, and any binary division rate. The clock input of one device is simply connected to the last output of the previous device in the chain. The "reset" inputs are wired together. The division rates for long binary dividers are easy to work out. Start with a value of one, and multiply by two for every binary divider in the chain.

There are several other CMOS binary counters, and these have more than seven stages, but some of them do not have the outputs of all the stages externally accessible. It is usually some of the early stages which do not have their outputs available. This is obviously of no importance if you are using the device as a divider and only require one of the later outputs. On the other hand, if a true binary counter is required, a device which does not provide access to every stage will almost certainly be unsuitable.

This is not really the place for a detailed discussion of CMOS binary counters, but the 74HCT4020 is worthy of mention. This is a very useful binary divider which has fourteen stages. However, the outputs of stages two and three are not accessible. In divider applications binary division rates of up to 16384 are available. Connection details for the 74HCT4020 are provided in Figure 4.11. This device will operate with input frequencies of up to 40MHz, and it has a Schmitt trigger at the clock input.

When dealing with binary counters you may encounter the terms "synchronous" and "asynchronous". Most binary counters (including the ones mentioned here) are of the asynchronous variety. This means that there is a short delay from one stage to the next. The practical significance of this is that where an increment in the count dictates that two or more outputs must change state, they will not change state at exactly the same time. This is not usually of importance, but it can cause erratic operation in some critical applications. A synchronous counter is one that includes circuits to equalise the delays from the input to each output, so that the outputs always change state in unison.

Divide by Ten

Many applications require a circuit that provides a divide by ten action. This is a division rate which is obviously not

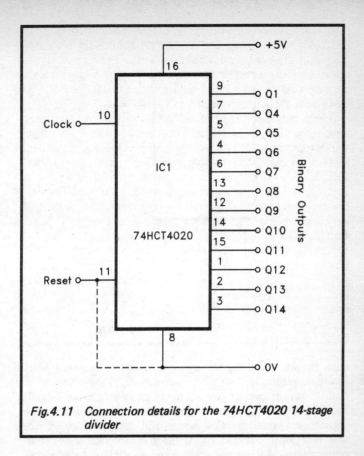

Fig.4.11 Connection details for the 74HCT4020 14-stage divider

available from a binary divider chain, which gets no nearer than division rates of eight and sixteen. It is possible to obtain a division rate of ten by using a binary counter plus some extra logic circuitry. The basic idea is to have a circuit that detects when the binary pattern on the counter has reached a count of five (101 in binary). This decoder circuit then resets the counter to zero, and switches the output of a flip/flop to the opposite logic level. This action continues indefinitely, with the output of the flip/flop being toggled after every five input pulses. The required divide by ten action is therefore obtained,

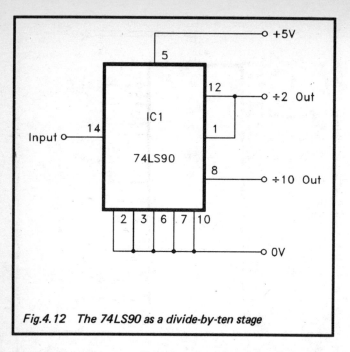

Fig.4.12 The 74LS90 as a divide-by-ten stage

with the output going through one complete cycle for every ten input pulses.

In practical circuits there is no point in producing a divide by ten circuit from a binary divider plus some external decoding circuitry, since there are several TTL devices which provide this function. The 74LS90 is the standard choice for most applications, as it is simple to use and is relatively inexpensive. In a simple divide by ten application it is used in the manner shown in Figure 4.12.

When used with this method of connection the basic action of the 74LS90 is to provide divisions by two and by five. By using the two stages in series a division by ten is obtained. In Figure 4.12 the division by two is obtained first, and then the division by five. A divide by ten action is, of course, still obtained if the two divider stages are swopped over (Figure 4.13). There are a couple of significant differences if this second method of connection is adopted. The obvious one is

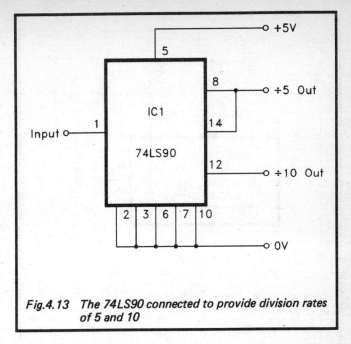

Fig.4.13 *The 74LS90 connected to provide division rates of 5 and 10*

that the output frequency from the first stage is one-fifth of the input frequency, whereas previously it was half the input frequency. In many cases this extra output frequency will not be needed, and either circuit will give the desired result.

The second difference is that the final output from the circuit of Figure 4.12 is not a squarewave, whereas the final output from the circuit of Figure 4.13 has an accurate 1:1 mark-space ratio. This is due to the fact that the output from the divide by two stage, as one would expect, has a 1:1 mark-space ratio, but the divide by five circuit has a 2:3 mark-space ratio. A divided by five signal having a mark-space ratio of 1:4 is available at pin 11. Divisions by odd numbers usually produce uneven mark-space ratios incidentally. This is inevitable if the output switches state after a certain number of complete input cycles. In many applications the precise shape of the output signal is unimportant, but this is a factor that should be borne in mind. If it is important for the

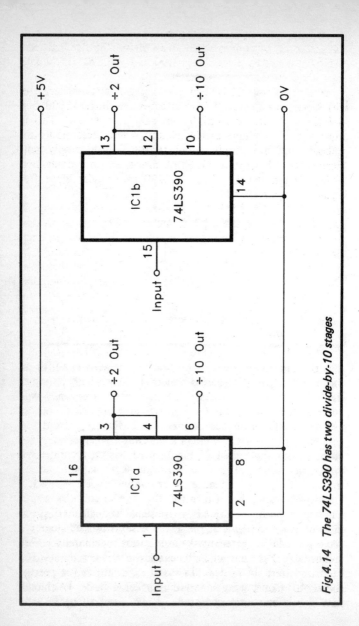

Fig. 4.14 The 74LS390 has two divide-by-10 stages

divided by ten signal to have a 1:1 mark-space ratio, the 74LS90 must be connected to give a division by five first, and then a division by two. The 7490 and 74LS90 can handle input frequencies of up to 42MHz.

Where several divide by ten stages are needed the 74LS390 can be used. This is effectively a dual 74LS90, but it lacks some of the 74LS90's set and reset inputs. This is unimportant in simple divider circuits where these inputs are unused, and are simply wired to the 0 volt supply rail. Figure 4.14 shows the 74LS390 connected to provide two divide by ten stages. The 74LS390 can handle input frequencies of up to 35MHz.

The 74LS92 has identical pinouts to the 74LS90, and it appears to provide the same function. In fact it provides a slightly different action due to differences in the internal circuit that resets the main binary counter. This results in the main counter giving a division rate of six rather than five. This device can therefore provide division rates of two, six, and twelve. Figure 4.15 shows connection details for the 74LS92 as a divide by two and divide by twelve counter. Note that the output from the divide by six stage has a 1:1 mark-space ratio.

The 74LS92 is probably most useful when it is used as a divide by six stage. In order to provide an output at one cycle per minute from a 1Hz clock signal a divide by 60 circuit is needed. The same division rate is needed to produce one cycle per hour from an input at one cycle per minute. A divide by 60 action is easily obtained by using a 74LS90 divide by ten circuit in series with a 74LS92 divide by six type. Figure 4.16 shows the circuit for a 74LS90/92 divide by 60 circuit.

Crystal Calibrator

The circuit of Figure 4.17 is for a simple but effective crystal calibrator or timebase generator. A crystal calibrator is a piece of equipment which generates one or more accurate frequencies that can be used to check the tuning accuracy of a radio receiver. A very basic crystal calibrator can consist of something like a simple 1MHz crystal oscillator. Although having just one output frequency may seem to be of little

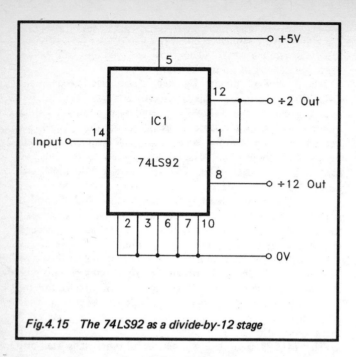

Fig.4.15 The 74LS92 as a divide-by-12 stage

practical value, circuits of this type are designed to have output signals that are rich in harmonics (multiples of the fundamental frequency). Thus, a 1MHz calibration oscillator will also produce output signals at 2MHz, 3MHz, 4MHz, etc. Most calibration oscillators produce reasonably strong output signals at frequencies of up to at least 30MHz, making them suitable for use throughout the short wave bands.

This calibration unit has IC1 as a 6MHz crystal oscillator, with trimming of the output frequency provided by C1. Use a 22p fixed value capacitor here if this facility is not required. It is useful to have at least one relatively high calibration frequency, as this provides harmonics that are well spaced out, and easily identified. With a maximum output frequency of 6MHz it should be easy to identify the harmonics, even at the upper limit of the short wave range. IC2 is a 74LS92 which is used here as a divide by six circuit to provide an output signal at 1MHz.

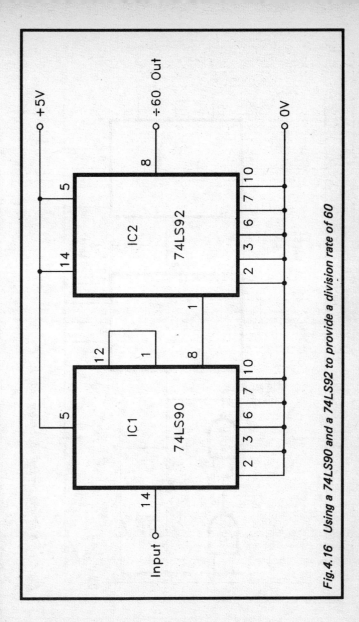

Fig. 4.16   Using a 74LS90 and a 74LS92 to provide a division rate of 60

105

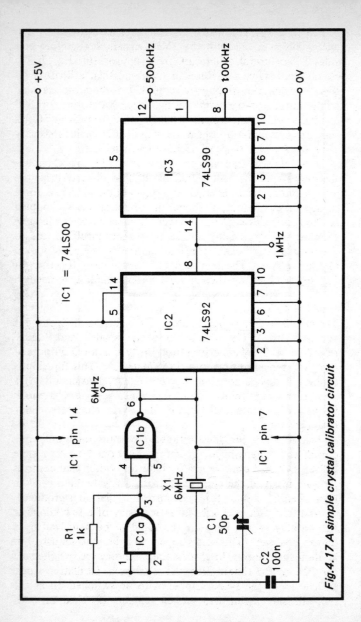

Fig.4.17 A simple crystal calibrator circuit

IC3 is a 74LS90 which is used here as a divide by ten circuit which is fed with the 1MHz signal. It therefore provides a very useful calibration frequency of 100kHz. IC2 is connected to give a division by two and then a division by five. A calibration frequency of 500kHz is therefore available at the output of the divide by two stage. A further 74LS90 could be used to process the 100kHz signal to provide 50kHz and 10kHz calibration signals. Using divider chains it is easy to produce a wide range of useful frequencies.

If the unit is used as a timebase for a TTL digital circuit, the outputs of the unit would be used to directly drive the main circuit. If it is used as a calibration oscillator for a radio receiver the output should only be very loosely coupled to the aerial socket of the receiver. In most cases an adequate coupling is obtained by connecting a short insulated lead to the output of the calibrator, and another to the aerial socket of the receiver. The two leads are placed close together, or can be twisted together if a stronger coupling is needed.

Heads or Tails

The circuit of Figure 4.18 simulates the tossing of a coin. D1 and D2 are l.e.d.s which represent "heads" and "tails" respectively. They are driven from the Q and not Q outputs of one "D" type flip/flop in a 74LS74 (IC2). This flip/flop is connected to operate as a simple divide by two circuit. IC1 acts as a gated clock oscillator which provides a clock frequency of around 5kHz, but the exact clock frequency is unimportant.

The flip/flop provides anti-phase outputs, and only one output at a time is high. Therefore, only one l.e.d. at a time will be switched on. S1 is a push-button switch that controls the gate input of the clock oscillator. The gate input is taken high when S1 is operated, and normal oscillation is produced.

As the circuit oscillates at a frequency of a few kilohertz the flashing of the l.e.d.s is too rapid to be perceived by a human observer. The l.e.d.s appear to light continuously, but at about half normal brightness (because they are switched off for 50% of the time). When S1 is released, oscillation stops. Whichever of the l.e.d.s happened to be switched on at the moment the circuit was broken remains switched on. Of

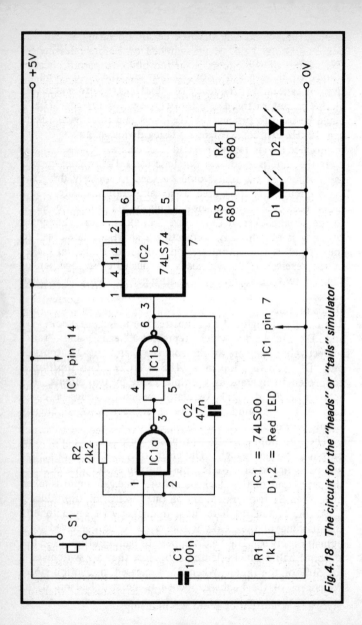

Fig.4.18 The circuit for the "heads" or "tails" simulator

108

course, there is no way that the person operating S1 can wait for a particular l.e.d. to be switched on before releasing S1. The action of the circuit is far too quick to permit cheating of this kind. The output signal is a squarewave signal having a very accurate one to one mark-space ratio, which means that the chances of producing a "heads" result are the same as those of producing a "tails" result. The unit should therefore give an accurate simulation of a coin being tossed.

Standard and LS TTL integrated circuits are capable of providing reasonably high output currents, and in this respect they are definitely superior to 4000 series CMOS devices with their high output resistances. The l.e.d. current in this circuit is not very high, and is actually only about 2 milliamps. These days it is possible to obtain good l.e.d. brightness using a l.e.d. current as low as this. Various high efficiency l.e.d.s are available at reasonable prices, and these give quite high light output levels from quite low drive currents. Many of these l.e.d.s will give excellent brightness from drive current of two milliamps. However, if necessary the l.e.d. current can be substantially boosted by decreasing the value of R3 and R4. A value of 330R for instance, will give a l.e.d. current of about 4 milliamps.

The output stages of TTL logic devices are not symmetrical. One practical result of this is that a low output level produces a potential that is very close to the 0 volt supply voltage, but high output level usually gives a voltage that is well short of the +5 volt rail. A high output level often results in a potential of about 3 volts or so. With almost 2 volts needed to switch on a l.e.d., quite low value series resistors are needed in order to drive a l.e.d. at currents of more than a few milliamps. Values as low as 120R seem to be quite acceptable, and provide l.e.d. currents of up to about 10 milliamps.

It is perfectly acceptable to drive l.e.d.s in the manner shown in the "heads" or "tails" circuit of Figure 4.19. Of course, if this method is used, a l.e.d. is switched on when the output driving it goes low, and switched off when the output goes high. The voltage across the series resistors is much higher using this method, and it is something in the region of 2.7 to 2.9 volts. A 330R series resistor therefore gives a l.e.d. current of about 8.5 milliamps.

109

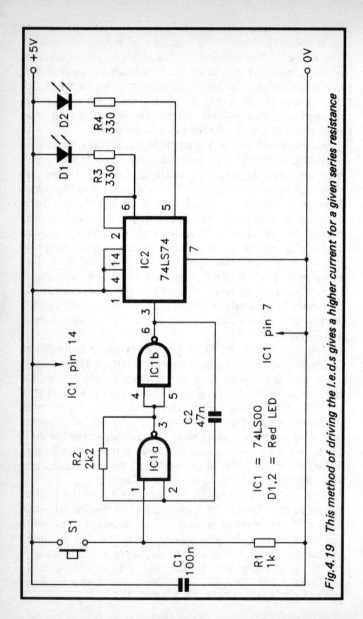

Fig.4.19 This method of driving the l.e.d.s gives a higher current for a given series resistance

110

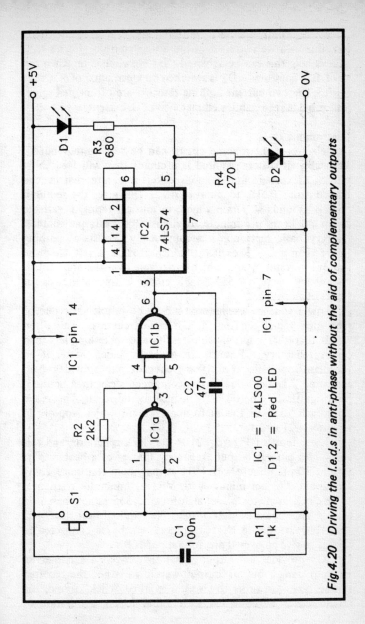

Fig.4.20 Driving the l.e.d.s in anti-phase without the aid of complementary outputs

Where complementary outputs are not available it is possible to drive two l.e.d.s from a single output. Figure 4.20 shows how this can be achieved. D1 is switched on when pin 5 of IC2 goes low — D2 is switched on when pin 5 of IC1 goes high. The two current limiting resistors are of unequal value, but provide reasonably well matched l.e.d. currents.

Metronome

An electronic metronome circuit can be very simple indeed. Basically all that is required is a circuit that will feed short pulses of current into a loudspeaker at a rate that can be varied from 0.5Hz to almost 5Hz. This gives the required "click" sounds at a rate which, in musical terms, is variable from 30 beats per minute to almost 300 beats per minute. A very basic metronome circuit usually consists of nothing more than a C — R oscillator which provides a suitable pulse output waveform, and which is variable over the appropriate frequency range. A 555 astable circuit is a popular basis for units of this type.

Low frequency oscillators tend to be problematic due to the high values required in the timing circuits. This often leads to rather unpredictable results and something less than good reliability. Results are generally much better if an oscillator operating at a higher frequency plus a divider chain are used. Lower value timing components can then be used, and significantly better performance should result. This is the approach used in the metronome circuit which appears in Figures 4.21 and 4.22.

The circuit of Figure 4.21 is the clock generator, and this produces a final output frequency that gives a beat rate of about 30 per minute with VR1 at maximum resistance, rising to about 270 per minute with VR1 at minimum resistance. The clock oscillator is a straightforward 555 astable based on IC1. This operates at 100 times the required beat rate. IC2 and IC3 are divide by ten circuits which are connected in series to give an overall division rate of 100.

IC3 provides an output signal that covers a suitable frequency range, but its output waveform is not the required pulse type. In order to give the required "click" sounds the loudspeaker must be fed with pulses having a duration of

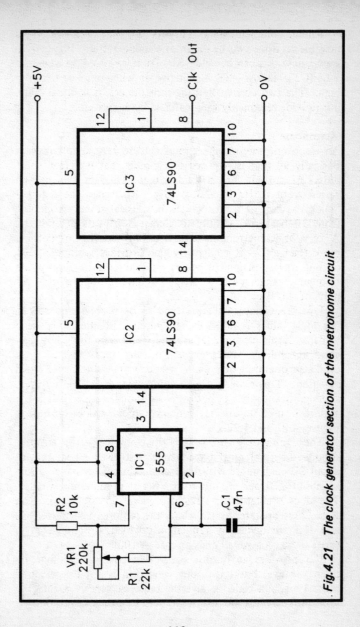

Fig.4.21   The clock generator section of the metronome circuit

113

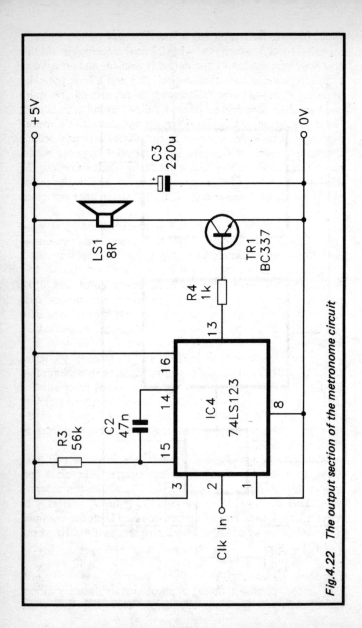

Fig.4.22 The output section of the metronome circuit

114

about one millisecond or less. The necessary pulse shaping is provided by IC4, which is a 74LS123 dual monostable. In this case only one section of the device is needed, and no connections are made to the other section. R3 and C2 set the pulse duration at around one millisecond, which should give quite good results. If a higher pitched "click" sound is preferred, reduce the value of C2. However, do not make this component very much lower in value as this would seriously reduce the volume level. IC4 is used in the positive triggered mode, but in this application it does not really matter whether the monostable is triggered on the positive or negative edges of the clock signal. Either way, IC4 will trigger once per clock cycle.

The output current from IC4 is inadequate to give good volume from a loudspeaker. TR1 is therefore used as a simple common emitter switch that drives the loudspeaker with a large current pulse each time IC4 is activated. Although LS1 is pulsed with a current of a few hundred milliamps, due to the high mark-space ratio of the output signal, the current consumption of the circuit is not very high. It is little more than the current drawn by the four integrated circuits (about 38 milliamps).

For a metronome to be really useful its frequency control must be fitted with a scale calibrated in beats per minute. Finding the calibration points normally means using a lot of trial and error, with the beat rate being determined simply by counting the number of beats in (say) a period of 30 seconds. Multiplying by two then gives the beat rate in beats per minute.

With this design there is a quick alternative if you have access to a suitable digital frequency meter. The clock frequency is 100 times the beat rate, and is within the accurate measurement range of many digital frequency meters. In order to set a beat rate of 60 per minute (1Hz) for example, VR1 would be adjusted to give a frequency of 100Hz at pin 3 of IC1.

Electronic Timer
For simple electronic timing applications an ordinary monostable circuit is perfectly adequate. However, long pulse

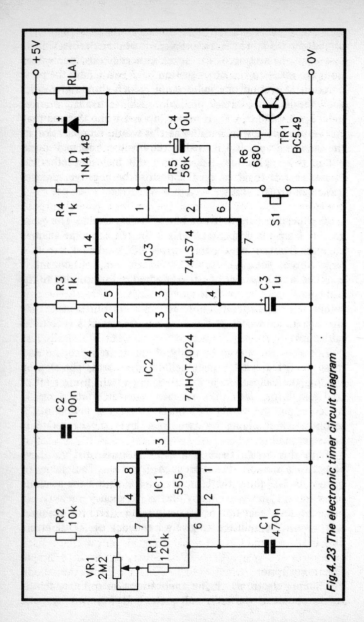

Fig.4.23 The electronic timer circuit diagram

116

durations are problematic, in the same way that low frequency oscillation tends to cause problems. In both cases it is necessary to resort to large capacitance and resistance values in the timing circuits, and results can be unpredictable.

An oscillator and a divider chain provides superior results in low frequency astable applications, and a similar arrangement can be used to good effect in timing applications that require long pulse durations. There is a slight complication in a monostable application in that only one output half cycle is required. This just necessitates the inclusion of some simple control logic to start and stop the counting process at the appropriate times.

Figure 4.23 shows the circuit diagram for a general purpose timer which uses an oscillator plus a divider chain. The oscillator is a simple 555 astable based on IC1, and the divider chain is a seven stage binary type (IC2). The latter is a 74HCT4024, but the 74HC4024 is easier to obtain and I found that this worked just as well with no compatibility problems.

The control logic circuit is built around one of the "D" type flip/flops in IC3. The other flip/flop of IC3 is left unused. The flip/flop is connected to give what is basically just a divide by two action, but the set and reset inputs are also utilized. R3 and C3 provide a set pulse to the flip/flop at switch-on. This takes the Q output high, which resets IC2. Operating S1 activates the reset input of IC3 via a simple "debouncing" circuit. The Q output then goes low, and IC2 is able to count normally. After 128 clock cycles the Q output of IC3 is taken back to the high state, and IC2 is reset to zero again. The Q output therefore goes low for 128 clock cycles each time S1 is operated. With the specified values in the clock oscillator this gives a timing range which extends from just under 5 seconds with VR1 at maximum resistance, to nearly 90 seconds with VR1 at maximum resistance.

The not Q output goes high for 128 clock cycles each time S1 is operated, and it is the signal from this output that is used to control the relay. The relay coil is driven via a simple common emitter switch (TR1). D1 is a protection diode which suppresses the high reverse voltage spike which is generated across the relay coil each time it is switched off.

Semiconductor devices are very intolerant of high voltages, and unless these voltage spikes are suppressed they are almost certain to cause some damage. The relay can be any type having suitable contacts, plus a coil that will operate reliably from a 5 volt supply, and a coil resistance of 50 ohms or more.

A relay may seem to be a rather old fashioned method of control, but relays still have their advantages. One is that the resistance through closed relay contacts is negligible, giving no significant power loss. A relay can handle a.c. and d.c. loads equally well, and heavy duty types can control very high power levels. The main advantage in many practical applications is that the control circuit is electrically isolated from the load. This is particularly important in applications where a mains powered load is being controlled. For reasons of safety it is essential that the main circuit is fully isolated from the dangerous mains supply.

In many digital applications the resolution of the circuit is an important matter. In this case, the length of one clock cycle has a significant bearing on the accuracy of the circuit. When S1 is activated, IC2 may be incremented to a count of one almost immediately, or it could take almost one complete clock period for it to increment. This depends on where the clock oscillator happens to be in its cycle at the instant S1 is operated. With each timing period taking 128 clock cycles, variations in the timing periods should be less than plus and minus one percent. If greater accuracy was required, adding a divide by ten circuit between IC1 and IC2 and reducing C1 to 47n would give a tenfold increase in resolution. Variations in the output times should then be well under plus and minus 0.1 percent.

Chapter 5

DECODING

It is often necessary to have a logic circuit that will detect a certain set of input states. Probably the most common application of these decoder circuits is in computers, and computer add-ons. Microprocessors use a bidirectional data bus to send data to peripheral circuits, and to read data from them. When data is written to a peripheral device a certain set of states will appear on the address and control buses. The peripheral circuit must include a decoder circuit to detect that the correct set of input states is present. The decoder produces an output pulse for the very brief period that the correct set of input levels is present.

If the microprocessor writes data to the peripheral circuit, this pulse is used to latch the data into a set of flip/flops. The data latch is sometimes within a special computer interfacing chip of some kind, but this function is often provided by a TTL chip. Data latching is a subject we will consider in more detail later in this chapter. During read operations the pulse from the decoder circuit is used to activate a set of tristate buffers. The buffers then place the data onto the data bus, and it is read by the microprocessor.

Decoder circuits of this type are not only needed in computing. Many types of digital processing circuit have to detect when a certain binary value is present on a set of data lines. The circuit then provides some form of processing on the data. Decoders are vital in many logic circuit applications.

Using gates to provide simple decoding was covered in earlier chapters. Gates are not always the best choice though. It is often better to resort to special decoder devices in applications where more than two or three input lines must be decoded. In this chapter we will consider some of these decoder chips, and we will also consider TTL devices that are suitable for use in computer input and output ports (octal flip/flops, octal tristate buffers, etc.).

Gates

Although special decoder chips are the best choice for many decoding applications, gates represent the best option in some cases. Gate type TTL decoders are often based on a 74LS30 8 input NAND gate and a 74LS14 hex trigger/inverter. The output of the gate will be low if all eight inputs are taken high, but will go high with any other set of input states. Adding an inverter ahead of an input results in that input being decoded to the low state. In the example decoder circuit of Figure 5.1, inputs 0, 2, 4, 6, and 7 are therefore decoded to the high state. Inputs 1, 3, and 5 are decoded to the low state.

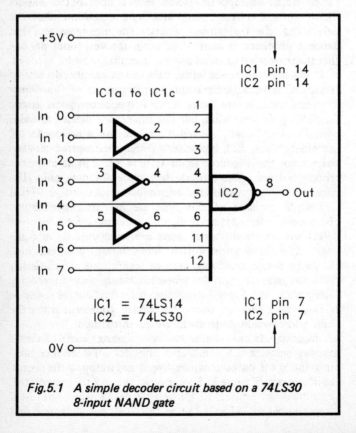

Fig.5.1   A simple decoder circuit based on a 74LS30 8-input NAND gate

One advantage of a simple gate decoder of this type is that it is very rapid in operation. It is also quite cheap as it only requires two simple TTL chips. The main drawback for amateur users is that although the circuit is quite simple, it often requires a fairly complex circuit board in order to implement the circuit in practice. Specialist decoder chips are often less demanding in this respect, and usually represent more practical choices.

Comparators

Digital comparators are popular for decoding applications. They can be wired to decode any set of input states, and are easily rewired to decode a different binary pattern. The basic idea is to have two sets of inputs. The binary pattern that must be decoded is hard wired onto one set of inputs. The other set of inputs is fed from the lines that must be decoded. An output of the decoder is activated when the two sets of inputs are fed with the same binary pattern.

The most simple of the TTL digital comparators is the 74LS85. Figure 5.2 provides connection details for this device. The 74LS85 decodes four lines which are connected to inputs A0 to A3. Inputs B0 to B3 are hard wired with the binary pattern that must be detected. This is just a matter of connecting each input to the appropriate supply rail. The device is symmetrical, and it therefore works just as well if A0 to A3 are hard wired with the binary pattern, and B0 to B3 are fed from the input lines.

There are three output pins, and usually it is only the "A = B" output at pin 6 that is of interest. This goes high when there is a match on the two sets of inputs. The other two outputs are only needed when binary values are being compared. Pin 5 goes high when the value on A0 to A3 is greater than that on B0 to B3. Pin 7 goes high when the binary value on B0 to B3 is the greater of the two.

Eight inputs can be decoded by cascading two 74LS85s, as shown in Figure 5.3. This is basically just a matter of connecting the three outputs of the first comparator to the corresponding inputs (pins 2, 3, and 4) of the second comparator. It is then the outputs of the second device which are used. Any number of 74LS85s can be cascaded, but remember that

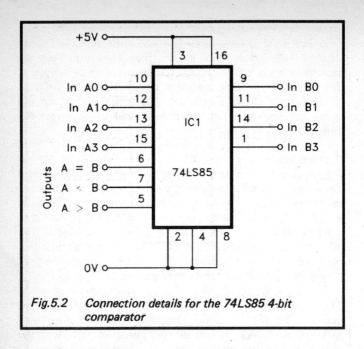

Fig.5.2   Connection details for the 74LS85 4-bit
comparator

signals are being passed from one device to the next. This
introduces propagation delays which reduce the operating
speed of the circuit. The greater the number of 74LS85s
that are cascaded, the longer the overall propagation delay.
The increase in the propagation delay is only about 11/13ns
per 74LS85, so using two or three devices in a decoder
circuit still provides reasonably fast operation.

The 74LS684 is suitable for decoding up to 8 input lines.
It is an 8 bit digital comparator, but it is somewhat simpler
than the 74LS85.   It lacks cascade inputs, and it is not
possible to wire two or three devices together in order to
provide decoding of 16 or 24 lines.   However, in decoder
applications some simple external gating is all that is needed
in order to combine the outputs of two or more 74LS684s
into a single output.   Connection details for the 74LS684s
are shown in Figure 5.4.

122

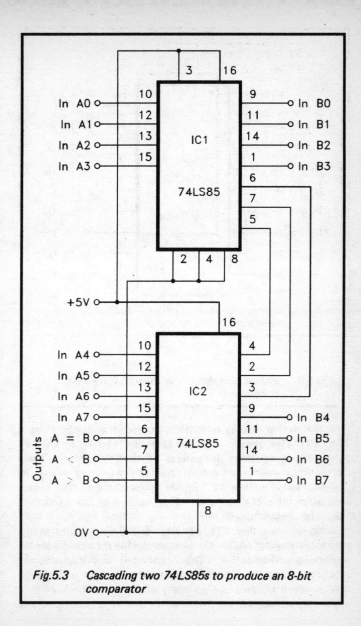

Fig.5.3   Cascading two 74LS85s to produce an 8-bit comparator

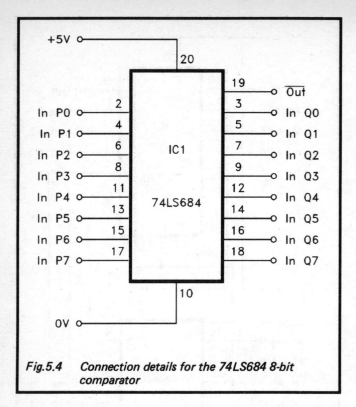

Fig.5.4 Connection details for the 74LS684 8-bit comparator

The output that is of interest in decoding applications is pin 19. This goes low when the binary pattern on the "P" inputs is identical to the pattern on the "Q" inputs. There is another output at pin 1, and this goes low when the binary value on the "P" inputs is greater than the binary value on the "Q" inputs. This output is not needed in decoder applications though.

There is another TTL eight bit digital comparator in the form of the 74LS688. Connection details for this device are provided in Figure 5.5. The 74LS688 is very similar to the 74LS684, and the two devices have virtually identical pinouts. The only difference is that pin 1 of the 74LS684 is a "P > Q" output, but on the 74LS688 it is a negative chip enable

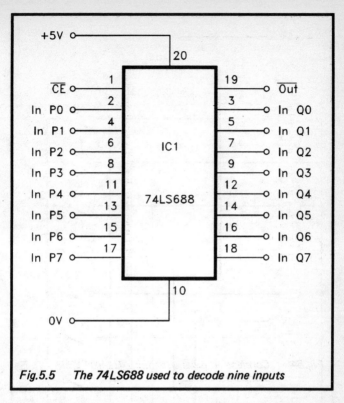

Fig.5.5   The 74LS688 used to decode nine inputs

input. This input is useful in decoder applications as it permits decoding of an extra input line. Even if the correct binary pattern is present on the main inputs, the output at pin 19 will only go low if pin 1 is low. This enables up to nine inputs to be decoded, and the only restriction is that pin 1 must be fed from a line which is to be decoded to the low state.

Input Selector

Comparators have a big advantage over other methods of decoding in that they are easily rewired to decode a different set of input states. Often the circuit boards are designed so that the comparator can be programmed to decode any

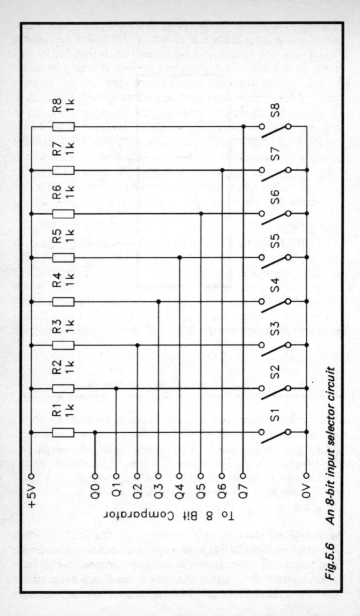

Fig.5.6 An 8-bit input selector circuit

126

desired binary code by installing the appropriate link wires. Another common method is to have a DIP switch unit on the board, and the appropriate binary pattern is then set on this bank of switches. This is the best method if it may be necessary to change the code from time to time, since it involves nothing more than altering the settings of a few switches.

Figure 5.6 shows the circuit diagram for an eight way input selector which is suitable for use with a 74LS684 or 74LS688, or any 8 bit comparator circuit. Obviously this circuit is easily altered to accommodate more or less inputs. One switch and one 1k pull-up resistor is needed per input. The inputs are normally taken high, but closing a switch takes the corresponding input low.

3 to 8 Line

The 74LS138 3 to 8 line decoder is a popular chip for decoding applications. There are three normal inputs, and eight outputs which are numbered from "0" to "7". Seven of the outputs are normally high, and one output is low. Which output goes low depends on the binary value fed to the three inputs. For those who are not familiar with the binary numbering system, Table 1 should help to clarify matters.

Table 1

Input 0	Input 1	Input 2	Low Output
Low	Low	Low	0
High	Low	Low	1
Low	High	Low	2
High	High	Low	3
Low	Low	High	4
High	Low	High	5
Low	High	High	6
High	High	High	7

Figure 5.7 shows connection details for the 74LS138 when it is used as a straightforward 3 to 8 line decoder. This device can be used in a variety of decoding and general control logic applications. It is one of the most used and most useful devices in the TTL range. It is especially useful in a decoder

127

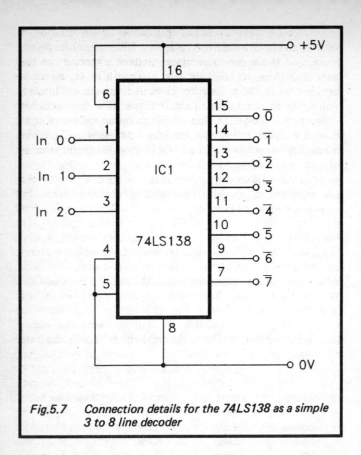

Fig.5.7 Connection details for the 74LS138 as a simple 3 to 8 line decoder

application as it provides several outputs without having to resort to a separate decoder for each set of logic levels that must be decoded.

Its usefulness is increased by the inclusion of a positive chip enable input at pin 6, and two negative chip enable inputs at pins 4 and 5. In a simple decoder application these are not required, and are connected to the appropriate supply rails. The device functions normally with these inputs at the correct logic levels. With one or more of them at the wrong logic level the chip is disabled, and all eight outputs go high.

In decoder applications the chip enable inputs can often be used to permit the 74LS138 to decode more than three inputs. Suppose that six inputs must be decoded, three to the high state and three to the low state. The three inputs to be decoded to the high state could be fed to pins 1, 2, and 6. The three inputs to be decoded to the low state could be connected to pins 3, 4, and 5. With the correct set of input levels the three chip enable inputs will be taken to the correct levels, and output 3 at pin 12 will go low. With any other set of input levels output 3 will be high.

In complex decoder applications one or more of the chip enable inputs can be fed from further decoding circuits. For example, a computer address decoder could have a 74LS684 decoding eight lines, and a 74LS138 decoding 3 lines. The output of the 74LS684 is normally high, and goes low when the correct set of input levels is detected. It would therefore be connected to a negative chip enable input of the 74LS138. This would permit 11 address/control lines to be decoded, or 13 if the spare chip enable inputs of the 74LS138 were also utilized.

The 74LS138 is popular for use in computer address decoder circuits where it is often used to decode the three least significant address lines. Each of the eight outputs then corresponds to a different address, and a different input or output port can be controlled from each of the eight outputs. Even if only one port is required, a 74LS138 can still be useful as part of the address decoder. It is sometimes necessary to have a means of altering the port address so that conflicts with other peripheral circuits can be avoided. Digital comparators plus an input selector circuit offer one way of achieving this. The 74LS138 offers a simple alternative. It is used to decode the three least significant address lines, and then a link wire is used to connect one of its outputs to the main port circuit. An output which places the port at an otherwise unused address is selected.

It is worth mentioning the 74LS154 4 to 16 line decoder. This uses the method of connection shown in Figure 5.8. It is very much like the 74LS138, but it has four inputs, and 16 outputs numbered from "0" to "15". One output is low and the other 15 are high. Which output assumes the low state is

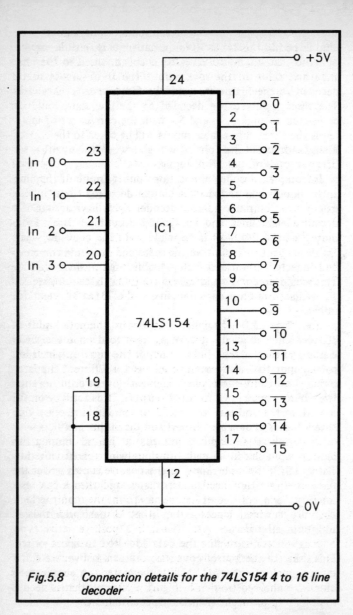

Fig.5.8 Connection details for the 74LS154 4 to 16 line decoder

determined by the four bit binary value on the inputs. Like the 74LS138, there are two negative chip enable inputs. However, there is no positive chip enable input. The 74LS138 is sufficient for most purposes, but the 74LS154 is very useful for applications which genuinely need more than eight outputs.

Data Latches

The use of "D" type flip/flops as data latches was discussed in Chapter 4. Computer and many other data latch applications require data to be handled in groups of eight bits (bytes). There are TTL devices which contain eight flip/flops and are specifically designed latching complete bytes of data. Probably the most useful of these is the 74LS273 octal "D" type flip/flop. This lacks some of the input and output terminals of full "D" type flip/flops, but it has all the functions that are necessary for operation as an eight bit data latch. Figure 5.9 shows connection details for the 74LS273 as an eight bit latch.

The eight bit input signal is applied to the data inputs of IC1, and the latched outputs are produced on the eight Q outputs. The latching pulse is applied to pin 11, which is a clock input that is common to all eight flip/flops. The latch input is normally high, and it is pulsed low in order to latch the current input level onto the outputs. It is actually on the low to high transition at the end of the latching pulse that the eight bits of data are "frozen" on the outputs.

A negative reset input is available at pin 1. Pulsing this input low results in all eight outputs being reset to the low state. Pin 1 is simply wired to the positive supply rail if the reset facility is not needed. In many applications the reset input is fed with the reset signal from the control logic circuit. The reset input of the 74LS273 must be fed via an inverter if the master reset signal is a positive active type. Some applications require the data latch to be reset at switch-on so that the outputs always start out at a known state, but do not require the reset facility thereafter. A simple reset circuit of the type shown in Figure 5.10 is all that is needed in order to give automatic resetting at switch-on.

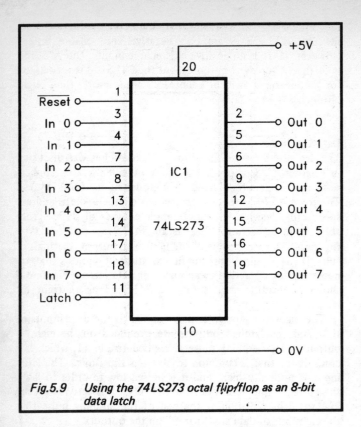

Fig.5.9   Using the 74LS273 octal flip/flop as an 8-bit
data latch

The 74LS374 is another octal "D" type flip/flop, and it has what is essentially the same pinout configuration as the 74LS273. The only difference between the two devices is that the reset input at pin 1 of the 74LS273 is replaced by a negative output enable input. The 74LS374 operates as a normal octal "D" type flip/flop with pin 1 taken low. With this input taken high the tristate outputs are taken to the "off" state.

The 74LS377 is another variation on the 74LS273. It again differs only in the function of pin 1. On the 74LS377 this is a negative chip enable input. Like the 74LS374, the device operates as a normal octal "D" type flip/flop with this input

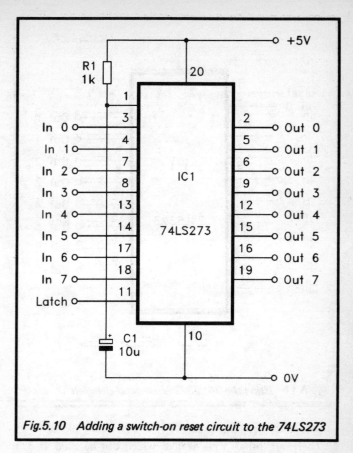

Fig.5.10 Adding a switch-on reset circuit to the 74LS273

taken low. The device ceases to function when pin 1 is taken high, and the tristate outputs go to the "off" state.

Although there may seem to be no real difference between the 74LS374 and the 74LS377, there is a crucial distinction. With pin 1 taken high, the outputs of both devices are switched off. However, the 74LS374 is still able to function as a data latch. Any new data latched into the device is stored internally and placed onto the outputs when pin 1 is taken low again. When pin 1 of the 74LS377 is taken high the device is disabled, and data can not be latched into the device

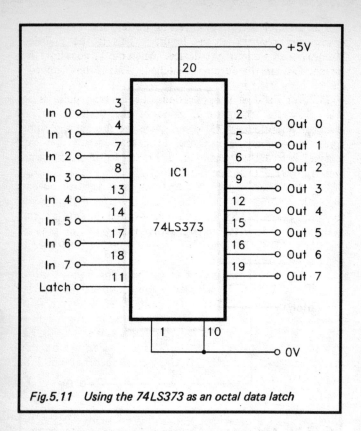

Fig.5.11   Using the 74LS373 as an octal data latch

until pin 1 is taken low again.

There are other TTL devices which can be used as data latches, and the 74LS373 is one of the most useful of these. This is an octal transparent latch, and Figure 5.11 provides connection details for this device.

There are one or two practical differences between this chip and the 74LS273. The most important of these is that fresh data is latched onto the outputs on a high to low transition at the latch input. Therefore, the latch input should be low under standby conditions, and pulsed high in order to latch fresh data onto the outputs. This is the opposite way round to the 74LS273. With the latch input high, the device acts as a simple octal non-inverting buffer, and the outputs follow any changes at the inputs. This is the so-called "transparent" mode of the device. When pin 11 goes low, the current data on the outputs is latched. This is the "latched" mode.

In most data latch applications the latching pulse is so brief that the "transparent" state of the device is of no practical importance. However, there are presumably some applications where it is useful to have a circuit that can transmit constantly changing data through to the output, and then latch the data at a certain instant.

On the 74LS373 pin 1 functions as a negative output enable input, like pin 1 of the 74LS374. The 74HCT533 is the same as the 74LS373, but it has inverted outputs (i.e. the outputs are the not Q outputs rather than the Q outputs of the flip/flops). This chip only seems to be available in high speed CMOS versions (HC and HCT).

The 74LS175 is useful for applications that require up to four bits of data to be latched. Connection details for the 74LS175 as a four bit data latch are provided in Figure 5.12. This is a quad "D" type flip/flop that is, in effect, half a 74LS273. It is used in basically the same way as a 74LS273. The not Q outputs of the flip/flops are accessible on this device, and not Q outputs Q0 to Q3 are available at pins 3, 6, 11, and 14 respectively.

Octal Inputs

Computing and other applications often require eight bit input ports. These are normally provided by octal tristate buffers. The outputs of the buffers are normally in the off state, and are activated by a pulse from the address decoder or some similar control circuit. The standard TTL octal tristate buffer is the 74LS244. Figure 5.13 shows connection details for this device. The enable input is a negative active type. Therefore, it should normally be in the high state, and it is taken low to activate the outputs. The eight buffers are all non-inverting types.

For the home constructor the 74LS244 can be a bit awkward to use as it has its inputs and outputs well mixed together. This can make it difficult to produce a printed

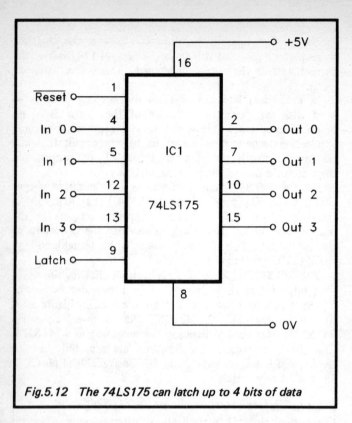

Fig.5.12   The 74LS175 can latch up to 4 bits of data

circuit board layout to accommodate this device. The 74LS245 octal transceiver has its inputs and outputs on opposite rows of pins, and is a much easier device to work with. Connection details for this component are provided in Figure 5.14. It is suitable for use on a bidirectional data bus, since the input and output functions can be swapped under the control of the send/receive input at pin 1. In this case pin 1 is simply wired to the 0 volt supply rail so that the device operates permanently in the "receive" mode. The 74LS245 provides non-inverted buffering.

The 74LS243 is suitable for applications that require tri-state buffering on up to four outputs. This is another

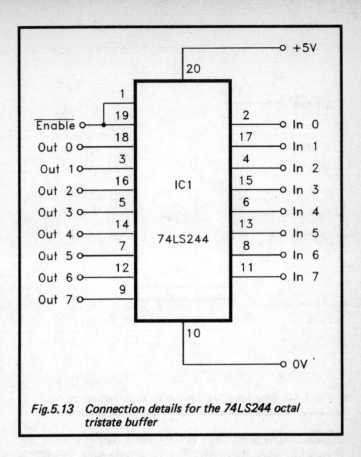

Fig.5.13   Connection details for the 74LS244 octal tristate buffer

transceiver, but Figure 5.15 shows how to use this device as a quad tristate buffer. This is another non-inverting device.

PC Port
Figure 5.16 shows how the 74LS688 can be used as an address decoder for a PC output port. The PCs have 16 bit address buses, but for input and output devices only the ten least significant address lines (A0 to A9) are utilized. Only two lines of the control bus need to be decoded. These are AEN and IOW. AEN goes low when any input or output port is

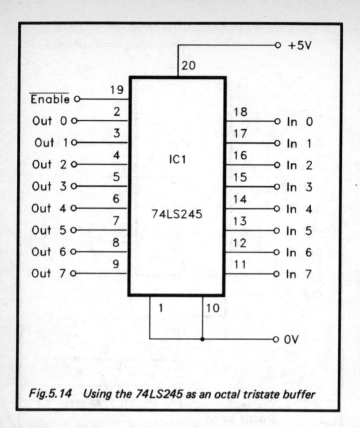

Fig.5.14   Using the 74LS245 as an octal tristate buffer

accessed. IOW is the write line for input/output devices, and
it goes low when data is written to a peripheral device. IOR is
the equivalent line for read operations incidentally.

In this decoder circuit IOW is decoded by the chip enable
input of IC1. Seven address lines (A3 to A9) and AEN are
decoded by the eight main inputs of IC1. The device is
programmed so that A8 and A9 are decoded to the high
state, while the other six lines are all decoded to the low
state.   The circuit gives less than full address decoding
because A0, A1, and A2 are not processed. A write operation to any input/output address in range &H300 to &H307
will activate the address decoder. Further decoding could be

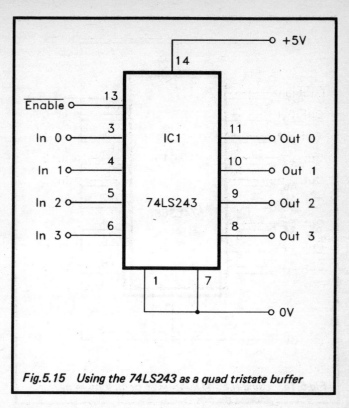

Fig.5.15   Using the 74LS243 as a quad tristate buffer

added, but in most address decoding applications something less than full address decoding is perfectly acceptable. This is due to the fact that there are normally far more addresses available than devices to occupy them.

A two chip PC output port can be produced by using the data latch circuit of Figure 5.17 with the address decoder of Figure 5.16. The latch uses a 74LS273 octal "D" type flip/flop in the manner described previously. C1 and R1 supply IC2 with a negative reset pulse at switch-on.

It should be possible to produce an eight bit input port by using the same address decoder, but with the IOR line of the PC expansion bus connected to pin 1 of the 74LS688. The output of the 74LS688 would be connected to pin 19 of

139

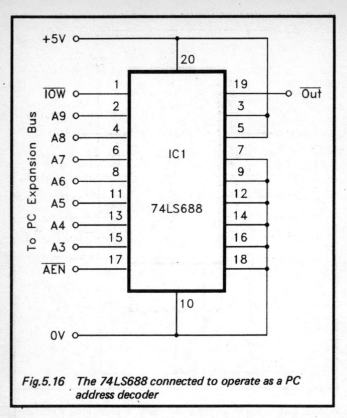

Fig.5.16 The 74LS688 connected to operate as a PC
address decoder

a 74LS245 connected as an octal tristate buffer (see Figure
5.14). The outputs of the 74LS245 would feed the lower
eight bits of the PC data bus.

TTL Power Supplies
TTL circuits are not ideal where operation from a battery
supply is needed. Even if LS TTL devices are used, the supply
current is likely to be rather high for economic battery operation. High speed CMOS devices are definitely a better choice
if battery operation is essential. Even these will not provide
a really low current drain if much of the circuit is operating
at high frequencies. The main difficulty when using TTL

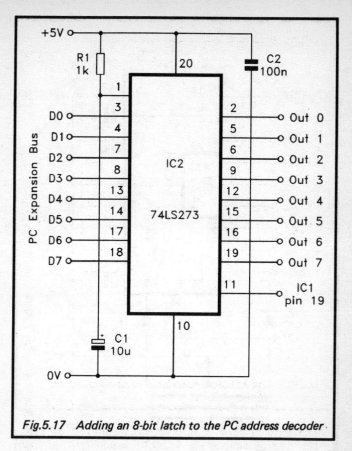

Fig.5.17   Adding an 8-bit latch to the PC address decoder

integrated circuits on a battery supply is that they require a reasonably stable 5 volts. Most types of battery can not supply a suitable voltage, and provide wide variations in output voltage during their normal operating life.

It is possible to run TTL circuits from a 6 volt supply provided by four ordinary "alkaline" batteries, but this is less than ideal. For the majority of the time the circuit will be operating from a supply voltage that is higher than the normal working level for TTL devices, and results might be a bit erratic. A circuit that is powered in this way should

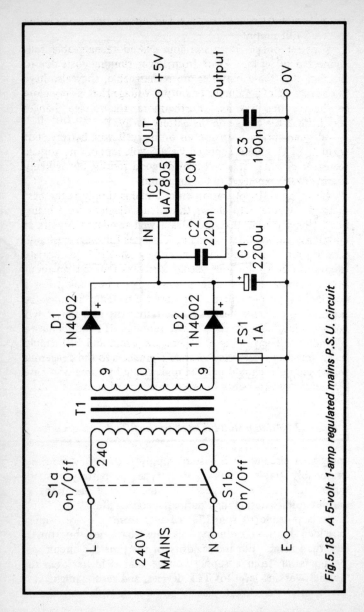

Fig.5.18 A 5-volt 1-amp regulated mains P.S.U. circuit

certainly not be connected to a TTL circuit that is operating from a 5 volt supply.

A better option is to use four NiCad rechargeable cells connected in series. Apart from lower running costs due to the fact that these batteries are rechargeable, they also have the advantage of producing an output voltage that is very close to the required 5 volts. Furthermore, the voltage changes very little as the charge on the battery decays.

Another option is to use an ordinary 9 volt battery, but with the TTL circuit supplied via a 5 volt monolithic voltage regulator circuit. This will provide good results, but is likely to prove very expensive in the long term.

Where possible, operation from a mains supply is the best method. Figure 5.18 shows the circuit diagram for a mains power supply unit that provides a well regulated 5 volts at currents of up to about one amp. This uses full-wave push-pull rectification, C1 to provide smoothing, and IC1 to regulate the output at 5 volts. For output currents of more than about 100 milliamps IC1 must be mounted on a heatsink. For a continuous output current of about one amp it must be mounted on a large heatsink. Note that the heat-tab of IC1 connects internally to the "COM" terminal. T1 should have a secondary current rating of at least one amp, and FS1 should be an anti-surge fuse. **As this circuit connects to the dangerous mains supply it should only be undertaken by those who have the necessary experience to tackle this type of circuit.**

Notes

Notes

Please note following is a list of other titles that are available in our range of Radio, Electronics and Computer books.

These should be available from all good Booksellers, Radio Component Dealers and Mail Order Companies.

However, should you experience difficulty in obtaining any title in your area, then please write directly to the Publisher enclosing payment to cover the cost of the book plus adequate postage.

If you would like a complete catalogue of our entire range of Radio, Electronics and Computer Books then please send a Stamped Addressed Envelope to:

BERNARD BABANI (publishing) LTD
THE GRAMPIANS
SHEPHERDS BUSH ROAD
LONDON W6 7NF
ENGLAND

160	Coil Design and Construction Manual	£2.50
227	Beginners Guide to Building Electronic Projects	£1.95
BP28	Resistor Selection Handbook	£0.60
BP36	50 Circuits Using Germanium Silicon & Zener Diodes	£1.95
BP37	50 Projects Using Relays, SCRs and TRIACs	£2.95
BP39	50 (FET) Field Effect Transistor Projects	£2.95
BP42	50 Simple LED Circuits	£1.95
BP44	IC 555 Projects	£2.95
BP48	Electronic Projects for Beginners	£1.95
BP49	Popular Electronic Projects	£2.50
BP53	Practical Electronics Calculations & Formulae	£3.95
BP56	Electronic Security Devices	£2.95
BP74	Electronic Music Projects	£2.95
BP76	Power Supply Projects	£2.50
BP78	Practical Computer Experiments	£1.75
BP80	Popular Electronic Circuits – Book 1	£2.95
BP84	Digital IC Projects	£1.95
BP85	International Transistor Equivalents Guide	£3.95
BP87	50 Simple LED Circuits – Book 2	£1.95
BP88	How to Use Op-amps	£2.95
BP90	Audio Projects	£2.50
BP92	Electronics Simplified – Crystal Set Construction	£1.75
BP94	Electronic Projects for Cars and Boats	£1.95
BP95	Model Railway Projects	£2.95
BP97	IC Projects for Beginners	£1.95
BP98	Popular Electronic Circuits – Book 2	£2.95
BP99	Mini-matrix Board Projects	£2.50
BP105	Aerial Projects	£2.50
BP107	30 Solderless Breadboard Projects – Book 1	£2.95
BP110	How to Get Your Electronic Projects Working	£2.95
BP111	Audio	£3.95
BP115	The Pre-computer Book	£1.95
BP118	Practical Electronic Building Blocks – Book 2	£1.95
BP121	How to Design and Make Your Own PCB's	£2.50
BP122	Audio Amplifier Construction	£2.95
BP125	25 Simple Amateur Band Aerials	£1.95
BP126	BASIC & PASCAL in Parallel	£1.50
BP130	Micro Interfacing Circuits – Book 1	£2.75
BP131	Micro Interfacing Circuits – Book 2	£2.75
BP132	25 Simple SW Broadcast Band Aerials	£1.95
BP136	25 Simple Indoor and Window Aerials	£1.75
BP137	BASIC & FORTRAN in Parallel	£1.95
BP138	BASIC & FORTH in Parallel	£1.95
BP144	Further Practical Electronics Calculations & Formulae	£4.95
BP145	25 Simple Tropical and MW Band Aerials	£1.75
BP146	The Pre-BASIC Book	£2.95
BP147	An Introduction to 6502 Machine Code	£2.95
BP148	Computer Terminology Explained	£2.95
BP171	Easy Add-on Projects for Amstrad CPC 464, 664, 6128 & MSX Computers	£2.95
BP176	A TV-DXers Handbook (Revised Edition)	£5.95
BP177	An Introduction to Computer Communications	£2.95
BP179	Electronic Circuits for the Computer Control of Robots	£2.95
BP182	MIDI Projects	£2.95
BP184	An Introduction to 68000 Assembly Language	£2.95
BP187	A Practical Reference Guide to Word Processing on the Amstrad PCW8256 & PCW8512	£5.95
BP190	More Advanced Electronic Security Projects	£2.95
BP192	More Advanced Power Supply Projects	£2.95
BP193	LOGO for Beginners	£2.95
BP196	BASIC & LOGO in Parallel	£2.95
BP197	An Introduction to the Amstrad PC's	£5.95
BP198	An Introduction to Antenna Theory	£2.95
BP230	A Concise Introduction to GEM	£2.95
BP232	A Concise Introduction to MS-DOS	£2.95
BP233	Electronic Hobbyists Handbook	£4.95
BP239	Getting the Most From Your Multimeter	£2.95
BP240	Remote Control Handbook	£3.95
BP243	BBC BASIC86 on the Amstrad PC's & IBM Compatibles – Book 1: Language	£3.95
BP244	BBC BASIC86 on the Amstrad PC's & IBM Compatibles – Book 2: Graphics and Disk Files	£3.95
BP245	Digital Audio Projects	£2.95
BP246	Musical Applications of the Atari ST's	£5.95
BP247	More Advanced MIDI Projects	£2.95
BP248	Test Equipment Construction	£2.95
BP249	More Advanced Test Equipment Construction	£3.50
BP250	Programming in FORTRAN 77	£4.95
BP251	Computer Hobbyists Handbook	£5.95
BP254	From Atoms to Amperes	£3.50
BP255	International Radio Stations Guide (Revised 1991/92 Edition)	£5.95
BP256	An Introduction to Loudspeakers & Enclosure Design	£2.95
BP257	An Introduction to Amateur Radio	£3.50
BP258	Learning to Program in C (Revised Edition)	£4.95
BP259	A Concise Introduction to UNIX	£2.95
BP260	A Concise Introduction to OS/2	£2.95
BP261	A Concise Introduction to Lotus 1-2-3 (Revised Edition)	£3.95

BP262	A Concise Introduction to Wordperfect (Revised Edition)	£...
BP264	A Concise Advanced User's Guide to MS-DOS (Revised Edition)	£3.95
BP265	More Advanced Uses of the Multimeter	£2.95
BP266	Electronic Modules and Systems for Beginners	£3.95
BP267	How to Use Oscilloscopes & Other Test Equipment	£3.50
BP269	An Introduction to Desktop Publishing	£5.95
BP270	A Concise Introduction to Symphony	£3.95
BP271	How to Expand, Modernise & Repair PC's & Compatibles	£4.95
BP272	Interfacing PC's and Compatibles	£3.95
BP273	Practical Electronic Sensors	£4.95
BP274	A Concise Introduction to SuperCalc5	£3.95
BP275	Simple Short Wave Receiver Construction	£3.95
BP276	Short Wave Superhet Receiver Construction	£2.95
BP277	High Power Audio Amplifier Construction	£3.95
BP278	Experimental Antenna Topics	£3.50
BP279	A Concise Introduction to Excel	£3.95
BP280	Getting the Most From Your PC's Hard Disk	£3.95
BP281	An Introduction to VHF/UHF for Radio Amateurs	£3.50
BP282	Understanding PC Specifications	£3.95
BP283	A Concise Introduction to SmartWare II	£4.95
BP284	Programming in QuickBASIC	£4.95
BP285	A Beginners Guide to Modern Electronic Components	£3.95
BP286	A Reference Guide to Basic Electronics Terms	£5.95
BP287	A Reference Guide to Practical Electronics Terms	£5.95
BP288	A Concise Introduction to Windows3.0	£3.95
BP290	An Introduction to Amateur Communications Satellite	£3.95
BP291	A Concise Introduction to Ventura	£3.95
BP292	Public Address Loudspeaker Systems	£3.95
BP293	An Introduction to Radio Wave Propagation	£3.95
BP294	A Concise Introduction to Microsoft Works	£4.95
BP295	A Concise Introduction to Word for Windows	£4.95
BP297	Loudspeakers for Musicians	£3.95
BP298	A Concise Introduction to the Mac System & Finder	£3.95
BP299	Practical Electronic Filters	£4.95
BP300	Setting Up An Amateur Radio Station	£3.95
BP301	Antennas for VHF and UHF	£3.95
BP302	A Concise Users Guide to Lotus 1-2-3 Release 3.1	£3.95
BP303	Understanding PC Software	£4.95
BP304	Projects for Radio Amateurs and SWLs	£3.95
BP305	Learning CAD with AutoSketch for Windows	£5.95
BP306	A Concise Introduction to Ami Pro 3	£4.95
BP307	A Concise Introduction to QuarkXPress	£4.95
BP308	A Concise Introduction to Word 5.1 on the Macintosh	£5.95
BP309	Preamplifier and Filter Circuits	£3.95
BP310	Acoustic Feedback – How to Avoid It	£3.95
BP311	An Introduction to Scanners and Scanning	£4.95
BP312	An Introduction to Microwaves	£3.95
BP313	A Concise Introduction to Sage	£3.95
BP314	A Concise Introduction to Quattro Pro	£4.95
BP315	An Introduction to the Electromagnetic Wave	£4.95
BP316	Practical Electronic Design Data	£4.95
BP317	Practical Electronic Timing	£4.95
BP318	A Concise User's Guide to MS-DOS 5	£4.95
BP319	Making MS-DOS Work for You	£4.95
BP320	Electronic Projects for Your PC	£3.95
BP321	Circuit Source – Book 1	£4.95
BP322	Circuit Source – Book 2	£4.95
BP323	How to Choose a Small Business Computer System	£4.95
BP324	The Art of Soldering	£3.95
BP325	A Concise Users Guide to Windows3.1	£4.95
BP326	The Electronics of Satellite Communications	£4.95
BP327	MS-DOS One Step at a Time	£4.95
BP328	Sage Explained	£5.95
BP329	Electronic Music Learning Projects	£4.95
BP330	A Concise User's Guide to Lotus 1-2-3 Release 2.4	£4.95
BP331	A Beginners Guide to MIDI	£4.95
BP332	A Beginners Guide to TTL Digital ICs	£4.95
BP333	A Beginners Guide to CMOS Digital ICs	£4.95
BP334	Magic Electronic Projects	£4.95
BP335	Operational Amplifier User's Handbook	£5.95
BP336	A Concise User's Guide to Lotus 1-2-3 Release 3.4	£5.95
BP337	A Concise Users Guide to Lotus 1-2-3 for Windows	£5.95
BP338	A Concise Introduction to Word for Windows	£5.95
BP339	A Concise Introduction to Wordperfect 5.2 for Windows	£5.95
BP340	A Concise Introduction to dBase V	£4.95
BP341	A Concise Users Guide to MS-DOS 6	£5.95
BP342	A Conciser Users Guide to Lotus Improv	£5.95